WORLDS OF WONDER

A Beka Book® Reading Program

A Beka Book®
A MINISTRY OF
PENSACOLA CHRISTIAN COLLEGE
PENSACOLA, FLORIDA 32523-9160

To Parents and Teachers

Children are eagerly searching for a workable sense of values. They need to see in the lives of great people, common people, and children like themselves, the unchanging values of the ages lived out. They need reading material that will give them ideals to reach for and examples to follow.

The stories in this reader have been selected from the readers of America's past and have been edited, modernized, and classroom-tested for student appeal and readability. This reader will introduce to children not only what is excellent in itself, but what their parents and grandparents have read before them—stories so good that they will never become old and stories that impart moral values.

Many values are taught throughout the book. Among them are honesty, integrity, courage, faith, kindness, forgiveness, industry, and patriotism.

Thought questions at the end of the stories greatly aid in the understanding and appreciation of the selections.

Editors *Laurel Hicks, Marion Hedquist, Shela Conrad, Debbie Beck*

Design *Michelle Johnson, Dawn Rash*

Art *Brian Jekel, Frank Hicks, Jim Hutchinson, Craig Granger, Omar Garcia, Terrilynn Broomall, Stephanie Bowstring*

Contents

Books* *Eleanor Farjeon* 1

The Monkey and the Crocodile
Retold by Ellen C. Babbitt 2

The Monkeys and the Crocodile
Laura E. Richards 12

The King and His Hawk
Retold by James Baldwin 14

Only the Stars and the Sea Gulls
Alice Geer Kelsey 22

The Town Crier and the Tailor *Maud Lindsay* 30

Thankfulness *Author Unknown* 38

The Lory Who Longed for Honey *Leila Berg* 39

Someone *Walter de la Mare* 52

Greedy Greta *Cookie Lambert Altizer* 53

The Woman Who Shared Her Last Loaf
The Bible, as told by William J. Sly 60

Missionary Penny *Author Unknown* 65

Prayer of a Child *Christina Rossetti* 70

Black Beauty's First Home *Anna Sewell* 71

Built For Speed *Tracie Cushman* 77

The Ride of Paul Revere
Retold by James Baldwin 89

How Lydia Darrah Served Her Country
Albert F. Blaisdale and Francis K. Ball 97

*Entries in italic type are poems.

America, Our Country   *Dorothy Hall* **107**

Nathan Hale   *Author Unknown* **108**

Washington and His Hatchet
Edward Eggleston **112**

Whopper   *Nan Gilbert* **114**

Storm at Sea   *Johann Wyss* **127**

A Lad of Long Ago
Caroline S. Bailey and Clara M. Lewis **147**

Lincoln   *Nancy Byrd Turner* **157**

Hector and His Conscience   *Almira Kirkham* **158**

Cornelius and His Bean Tree
Adapted by Mary Entwistle **167**

Little John Gray   *Author Unknown* **170**

Christmas with the Angels
Patricia M. St. John **172**

Nobody's Horse   *Louisa May Alcott* **187**

The Pasture   *Robert Frost* **201**

The Prisoner and the Shipwreck
The Bible, as told by William J. Sly **202**

A Good Traveller   *Frances Cavanah* **208**

A Lost Lamb   *Retold by James Baldwin* **218**

The Lost Lamb   *Author Unknown* **228**

King Canute on the Seashore
Retold by James Baldwin **230**

The Cricket in Times Square *George Selden* **235**

Who Taught Them? *Albert N. Raub* **250**

All Because of an Awl *Delores Shimmin* **251**

Kitten-in-a-Basket *Elizabeth Coatsworth* **259**

Suppose *Frances Hodgson Burnett* **271**

Lost in the Apple Cave *Carolyn Sherwin Bailey* **286**

The Rain Song *Robert Loveman* **301**

Any Old Junk Today? *Carolyn Haywood* **302**

Holding Hands *Lenore M. Link* **315**

The Hairy Dog *Herbert Asquith* **316**

Jonathan Bing *B. Curtis Brown* **317**

For the King *Sir Walter Scott (adapted)* **319**

Breakfast with Buffalo Bill *Carol Ryrie Brink* **326**

The Missionary with the Orange Hair
  Lois H. Hoadley **336**

One Gentle Word *Anonymous* **353**

Bedtime *Author Unknown* **354**

Credits **355**

Worlds of Wonder
Guide to Character-Building Story Themes

Cheerfulness

A Lost Lamb, p. 218

Common Sense

Cornelius and His Bean
Tree, p. 167

Compassion

Nobody's Horse, p. 187
The Lost Lamb, p. 228
Suppose, p. 271
The Missionary with the
Orange Hair, p. 336

Conscience

Little John Gray, p. 170
Christmas with the Angels,
p. 172
Whopper, p. 114

Contentment

The Town Crier and the
Tailor, p. 30

Courage

The Ride of Paul Revere, p. 89
How Lydia Darrah Served
Her Country, p. 97
Nathan Hale, p. 108
Kitten-in-a-Basket, p. 259
For the King, p. 319
The Missionary with the
Orange Hair, p. 336

Duty

Nathan Hale, p. 108

Encouragement

A Good Traveller, p. 208

Faith

Storm at Sea, p. 127
The Prisoner and the
Shipwreck, p. 202
The Missionary with the
Orange Hair, p. 336

Faithfulness

The King and His Hawk,
p. 14
Only the Stars and the
Sea Gulls, p. 22
A Good Traveller, p. 208

Family

Storm at Sea, p. 127
Christmas with the Angels,
p. 172

Forgiveness

Hector and His Conscience,
p. 158

Friendship

The King and His Hawk,
p. 14
Greedy Greta, p. 53
The Cricket in Times Square,
p. 235
Kitten-in-a-Basket, p. 259
Lost in the Apple Cave,
p. 286
Breakfast with Buffalo Bill,
p. 326

Gratitude
Storm at Sea, p. 127

Generosity
Greedy Greta, p. 53
The Woman Who Shared
Her Last Loaf, p. 60
Missionary Penny, p. 65
The Cricket in Times Square,
p. 235
Suppose, p. 271

Gentleness
Black Beauty's First Home,
p. 71

Helpfulness/Service
The Ride of Paul Revere,
p. 89
How Lydia Darrah Served
Her Country, p. 97
Nathan Hale, p. 108
Lost in the Apple Cave, p. 286

Honesty
Washington and His
Hatchet, p. 112
A Lad of Long Ago, p. 147
Hector and His Conscience,
p. 158
Whopper, p. 114

Humility
King Canute on the Seashore,
p. 230

Industry
Only the Stars and the
Sea Gulls, p. 22
A Lad of Long Ago, p. 147
Lost in the Apple Cave, p. 286

Integrity
Only the Stars and the Sea
Gulls, p. 22

Kindness
Greedy Greta, p. 53
The Woman Who Shared
Her Last Loaf, p. 60
A Lost Lamb, p. 218

Love/Loyalty
The King and His Hawk, p. 14
A Good Traveller, p. 208
For the King, p. 319

Obedience
Little John Gray, p. 170

Patriotism
The Ride of Paul Revere,
p. 89
How Lydia Darrah Served
Her Country, p. 97
Washington and His
Hatchet, p. 112
Nathan Hale, p. 108
For the King, p. 319

Perseverance
Built for Speed, p. 77

Resourcefulness
The Monkey and the
Crocodile, p. 2
The Lory Who Longed for
Honey, p. 39
Built for Speed, p. 77
All Because of an Awl, p. 251
Any Old Junk Today?, p. 302

Sacrifice

The King and His Hawk,
*   p. 14*
Nathan Hale, p. 108
Nobody's Horse, p. 187
Suppose, p. 271
For the King, p. 319
The Missionary with the
*   Orange Hair, p. 336*

Self-Control

The King and His Hawk,
*   p. 14*

Thoughtfulness

Greedy Greta, p. 53

Truthfulness

Whopper, p. 114

Pronunciation Key

Symbol • Example		Symbol • Example	
ā	āte	ng	song
â	dâre	ō	ōver
ă	făt	ô	côrd
ä	fäther	ŏ	nŏt
a	*a*bsorb	*o*	*o*bscure
ə	ago (ə·gō′)	oi	boil
ch	chin	o͞o	bro͞od
ē	ēven	o͝o	bo͝ok
ê	fêar	ou	out
ĕ	ĕgg	sh	shark
e	re*c*ent	th	thin
ễ	pondễr	tᵫ	virtᵫe
g	good	ū	ūnit
ī	īce	û	ûrn
ĭ	ĭt	ŭ	ŭp
i	clar*i*ty	*u*	fo*cus*
j	jog	zh	azure (zh = z)
ks	perplex (ks = x)	′	trifle (trī′f′l; shows that the vowel is not sounded)
kw	quart (kw = qu)		

Books

What worlds of wonder are our books!
As one opens them and looks,
New ideas and people rise
In our fancies and our eyes.

The room we sit in melts away,
And we find ourselves at play
With someone who, before the end,
May become our chosen friend.

Or we sail along the page
To some other land or age.
Here's our body in the chair,
But our mind is over *there*.

—*Eleanor Farjeon*

The Monkey and the Crocodile
Part 1

A monkey lived in a great tree on a river bank. In the river there were many Crocodiles. A Crocodile watched the Monkeys for a long time, and one day she said to her son: "My son, get one of those Monkeys for me. I want the heart of a Monkey to eat."

"How am I to catch a Monkey?" asked the little Crocodile. "I do not travel on land, and the Monkey does not go into the water."

"Put your wits to work, and you'll find a way," said the mother.

And the little Crocodile thought and thought.

At last he said to himself: "I know what I'll do. I'll get that Monkey that lives in a big tree on the river bank. He wishes to go across the river to the island where the fruit is so ripe."

So the Crocodile swam to the tree where the Monkey lived.

"Oh, Monkey," he called, "come with me over to the island where the fruit is so ripe."

"How can I go with you?" asked the Monkey. "I do not swim."

"No—but I do. I will take you over on my back," said the Crocodile.

The Monkey was greedy, and wanted the ripe fruit, so he jumped down on the Crocodile's back.

"Off we go!" said the Crocodile.

"This is a fine ride you are giving me!" said the Monkey.

"Do you think so? Well, how do you like this?" asked the Crocodile, diving.

"Oh, don't!" cried the Monkey, as he went under the water. He was afraid to let go, and he did not know what to do under the water.

When the Crocodile came up, the Monkey sputtered and choked. "Why did you take me under water, Crocodile?" he asked.

"I am going to kill you by keeping you under water," answered the Crocodile. "My mother wants Monkey-heart to eat, and I'm going to take yours to her."

"I wish you had told me you wanted my heart," said the Monkey, "then I might have brought it with me."

"How strange!" said the Crocodile. "Do you mean to say that you left your heart back there in the tree?"

"That is what I mean," said the Monkey. "If you want my heart, we must go back to

the tree and get it. But we are so near the island where the ripe fruit is, please take me there first."

"No, Monkey," said the Crocodile, "I'll take you straight back to your tree. Never mind the ripe fruit. Get your heart and bring it to me at once. Then we'll see about going to the island."

"Very well," said the Monkey.

But no sooner had he jumped onto the bank of the river than—whisk! up he ran into the tree.

From the topmost branches he called down to the Crocodile in the water below:

"My heart is way up here! If you want it, come for it, come for it!"

2.

The Monkey soon moved away from that tree. He wanted to get away from the Crocodile, so that he might live in peace.

But the Crocodile found him, far down the river, living in another tree.

In the middle of the river was an island covered with fruit trees.

Half-way between the bank of the river and the island, a large rock rose out of the water. The Monkey could jump to the rock, and then to the island. The Crocodile watched the Monkey crossing from the bank of the river to the rock, and then to the island.

He thought to himself, "The Monkey will stay on the island all day, and I'll catch him on his way home at night."

The Monkey had a fine feast, while the Crocodile swam about, watching him all day.

Toward night the Crocodile crawled out of the water and lay on the rock, perfectly still.

When it grew dark among the trees, the Monkey started for home. He ran down to the river bank, and there he stopped.

"What is the matter with the rock?" the Monkey thought to himself. "I never saw it so high before. The Crocodile is lying on it!"

But he went to the edge of the water and called: "Hello, Rock!"

No answer.

Then he called again: "Hello, Rock!"

Three times the Monkey called, and then he said: "Why is it, Friend Rock, that you do not answer me to-night?"

"Oh," said the Crocodile to himself, "the rock answers the Monkey at night. I'll have to answer for the rock this time."

So he answered: "Yes, Monkey! What is it?"

The Monkey laughed, and said: "Oh, it's you, Crocodile, is it?"

"Yes," said the Crocodile. "I am waiting here for you. I am going to eat you."

"You have caught me in a trap this time," said the Monkey. "There is no other way for me to go home. Open your mouth wide so I can jump right into it."

Now the Monkey well knew that when Crocodiles open their mouths wide, they shut their eyes.

While the Crocodile lay on the rock with his mouth wide open and his eyes shut, the Monkey jumped.

But not into his mouth! Oh, no! He landed on the top of the Crocodile's head, and then sprang quickly to the bank. Up he whisked into his tree.

When the Crocodile saw the trick the Monkey had played on him, he said: "Monkey, you have great cunning. You know no fear. I'll let you alone after this."

"Thank you, Crocodile, but I shall be on the watch for you just the same," said the Monkey.

1. Explain how the crocodile "put his wits to work."

2. Why did the crocodile take the monkey back to his tree on the river bank?

3. Why did the monkey like to go to the island?

4. Where did the crocodile wait for the monkey?

The Monkeys and the Crocodile

Five little monkeys
   Swinging from a tree;
Teasing Uncle Crocodile,
   Merry as can be.
Swinging high, swinging low,
   Swinging left and right:
"Dear Uncle Crocodile,
   Come and take a bite!"

Five little monkeys
    Swinging in the air;
Heads up, tails up,
    Little do they care.
Swinging up, swinging down,
    Swinging far and near:
"Poor Uncle Crocodile,
    Aren't you hungry, dear?"

Four little monkeys
    Sitting in the tree;
Heads down, tails down,
    Dreary as can be.
Weeping loud, weeping low,
    Crying to each other:
"Wicked Uncle Crocodile,
    To gobble up our brother!"

—*Laura E. Richards*

Genghis Khan (gĕng′gĭs kän)
conquered   game
prey   whirring

The King and His Hawk

Genghis Khan was a great king and warrior.

He led his army into China and Persia, and he conquered many lands. In every country, men told about his daring deeds.

One morning when he was home from the wars, he rode out into the woods to spend the day hunting with a larger group of his friends. The men rode out with light hearts, carrying their bows and arrows. Behind them came the servants with the hounds.

It was a merry party, and the woods rang with their shouts and laughter. They expected to carry much game home in the evening.

On the King's wrist sat his favorite hawk, for in those days hawks were trained to hunt. At a word from their masters they would fly up into the air and look around for prey. If they chanced to see a deer or a rabbit, they would swoop down upon it swiftly as an arrow.

All day long Genghis Khan and his hunts-men rode through the woods, but they did not find as much game as they expected. Toward evening they started for home. The king had often ridden through the woods, and he knew all the paths, so while the rest of the party took the shortest way, he went by a longer road through a valley between two mountains.

The day had been warm, and the king was very thirsty. His pet hawk had left his wrist and flown away. The king knew it would be sure to find its way home.

The king rode slowly along. He had once seen a spring of clear water near this pathway. If he could only find it now! But the hot days of summer had dried up all the mountain brooks.

At last, to his joy, he saw some water trickling down over the edge of a rock. He knew that there was a spring farther up. In the wet season, a swift stream of water always poured down here, but now it came only one drop at a time.

The king leaped from his horse. He took a little silver cup from his hunting bag and held it so as to catch the slowly falling drops.

It took a long time to fill the cup, and the king was so thirsty that he could hardly wait. At last it was nearly full. He put the cup to his lips and was about to drink.

All at once there was a whirring sound in the air, and the cup was knocked from his hands. The water was all spilled on the ground.

The king looked up to see who had done this thing. It was his pet hawk. The hawk flew back and forth a few times, and then alighted among the rocks by the spring.

The king picked up the cup and again held it to catch the trickling drops. This time he did not wait so long. When the cup was half full, he lifted it toward his mouth. But before it had touched his lips, the hawk swooped down again and knocked it from his hands.

And now the king began to grow angry. He tried again, and for the third time the hawk kept him from drinking.

The king was now very angry indeed.

"How do you dare to act so?" he cried. "If I had you in my hands, I would wring your neck!"

Then he filled the cup again. But before he tried to drink, he drew his sword.

"Now, Sir Hawk," he said, "this is the last time."

He had hardly spoken before the hawk

swooped down and knocked the cup from his hand. But the king was looking for this. With a quick sweep of the sword, he struck the bird as it passed.

The next moment, the poor hawk lay bleeding and dying at its master's feet.

"That is what you get for your pains," said Genghis Khan.

But when he looked for his cup, he found that it had fallen between two rocks, where he could not reach it.

"At any rate, I will have a drink from that spring," he said to himself.

With that he began to climb the steep bank to the place from which the water trickled. It was hard work, and the higher he climbed, the thirstier he became.

At last he reached the place. There indeed was a pool of water; but what was

that lying in the pool, and almost filling it?
It was a huge, dead snake of the most
poisonous kind.

The king
stopped. He forgot his thirst. He thought
only of the poor dead bird lying on the ground
below him.

"The hawk saved my life!" he cried, "and
how did I repay him? He was my best friend,
and I have killed him."

He climbed down the bank. He lifted the

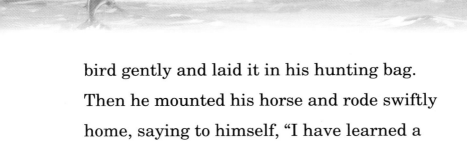

bird gently and laid it in his hunting bag. Then he mounted his horse and rode swiftly home, saying to himself, "I have learned a sad lesson today; and that is, never to do anything in anger."

Stop and Think

1. What weapons did the hunters take with them?

2. Why did the king take a hawk with him?

3. What happened each time the king tried to drink from his cup?

4. Why didn't the hawk want the king to drink the water?

The Bible Says,

"He that is soon angry dealeth foolishly."

Proverbs 14:17a

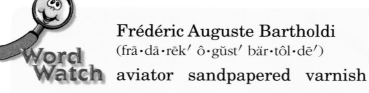

Word Watch

Frédéric Auguste Bartholdi
(frā·dā·rēk′ ô·gŭst′ bär·tôl·dē′)

aviator   sandpapered   varnish

generation   sculptor   proportions
freighters   mosquitoes

gunwales: the upper edge of the side of a ship
or boat

Only the Stars and the Sea Gulls

You could always count on Ryan to do the
right thing—when someone was watching.
He never threw erasers in school—when the
teacher was looking. He never let the air out
of the other fellows' bicycle tires—unless he
was sure they could not guess who did it.

You could always count on Ryan to do
good work—when it showed. His room was
always tidy—unless you peeked in the

22

dresser drawers or under the bed. His school papers had good marks—at least the ones he brought home.

One summer Ryan's Uncle Jack, who was an aviator, came for a visit. At first he thought Ryan was wonderful. Then he began to have surprises. There was the time, for instance, that Ryan and Uncle Jack were painting the canoe before a camping trip. First they sandpapered it all over to smooth out any rough spots. Then they patched the breaks and the weak spots. Then they sand-papered again, Uncle Jack working on one side of the canoe and Ryan on the other.

"Now we're ready for the paint on the outside and the varnish on the inside," said Ryan. He started to get the bending-over kinks out of his back.

Uncle Jack ran his hands over Ryan's

side of the canoe. He nodded that all was smooth and ready till he came to the places just under the gunwales.

"What's this?" Uncle Jack scraped off a lump of chewing gum, a flake of loose varnish, and a splinter of wood.

"There's another half hour's work getting your side ready."

"But who's going to look under the gunwales?" asked Ryan. "I've done a good job where it shows."

Uncle Jack just stood and looked at Ryan. "So *that's* your story! That explains a lot of things!"

Ryan squirmed. He thought Uncle Jack

would say a lot more. Instead, his uncle changed the subject suddenly. "Some day I'll take you for a plane ride."

Of course that was all right with Ryan. At last the day for the plane ride came. Ryan had thought of plenty of places he would like to see from the air, but Uncle Jack had just one idea.

"We are going to fly over New York Harbor," he announced. "Over the Statue of Liberty."

"I've see that lots of times," Ryan hinted. "I've been there by ferry boat. I've climbed way up to the balcony that runs around the head." But the Statue of Liberty was what Uncle Jack had decided Ryan should see from the air.

On the way to the airport Uncle Jack talked about Frédéric Auguste Bartholdi, the French sculptor who made the statue in 1886.

"It took a great man to dream a statue which would hold such meaning for generation after generation of people entering New York Harbor. It took a skilled sculptor to make such a gigantic figure and keep it in beautiful proportions. It took a careful workman to get every detail correct."

"Yeah," agreed Ryan, who had heard all this before.

"You may have my field glasses to look down at the top of the statue when we fly over it," said Uncle Jack. "Remember that in 1886 Bartholdi never dreamed people would be flying over his statue. In those days flying machines were just something to joke about. Bartholdi never expected anything but the stars and the sea gulls to look down on his statue, which would rise higher than the decks of ships in the harbor."

"I'll bet he didn't bother much with the

carving on the top of the statue," laughed Ryan, "It's a good joke on him to fly over it and look down on the part he thought wouldn't show."

Uncle Jack did not answer. He was busy tuning up his plane for the flight.

Soon they were up in the air, soaring over New York Harbor. The busy tugboats looked as though they came from a toy store. The low-lying freighters looked as though boys had made them from soapboxes. The sea gulls seemed like mosquitoes swooping about.

Ryan remembered to use his field glasses when they flew over the Statue of Liberty. He grinned at the trick they were playing on the famous sculptor of long ago, spying on what he thought would be out of sight.

The plane circled several times. Ryan had a long, clear look at the statue. His grin

faded. Uncle Jack smiled as he watched his
nephew's face in the mirror over the controls.
He knew what the boy was seeing. Every
hair on the top of the curly head of the Statue
of Liberty was as carefully carved as though
Frédéric Auguste Bartholdi, at work in 1886,
had known that airplanes would someday be
carrying people with field glasses over the top
of his statue. The great artist had done every
bit of his work well—even the parts that he
thought only the stars and the sea gulls
would ever
see.

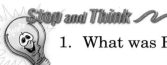

Stop and Think

1. What was Ryan's problem?

2. What project were Ryan and his Uncle Jack working on one day?

3. How did Uncle Jack learn about Ryan's problem?

4. What object did Uncle Jack take Ryan to see by air?

5. Why did Ryan expect to see poor workmanship on the top of the Statue of Liberty?

The Bible Says,

"And whatsoever ye do, do it heartily, as to the Lord, and not unto men."

Colossians 3:23

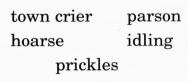

The Town Crier and the Tailor

There was once a town crier who was very sure that no one worked as hard as he. Why, with all his running up and down the streets to ring his bell and tell what was lost and what was found, and other news besides, his feet were ready to drop off, he said. And that was not the worst of it.

"Soon I shall have no more voice than a mouse's squeak," he told his friend, the tailor.

"Or a bear's growl, you had better say," answered the tailor, who for his part was sure that he worked harder than the crier any day. "If you sat cross-legged to sew a seam day in and day out, you would soon learn what hard work is," said he.

"Hard work!" exclaimed the crier. "Why, I never go by your shop in the wind and weather that I do not think what a warm corner and easy earnings a tailor has."

"And I never see you pass that I do not say to myself, 'There goes the crier with nothing to do but to make a noise,'" snapped the tailor.

The more they talked the crosser they grew, and they might be quarreling yet if they had not taken the matter to the parson, who was said to be the wisest man in town.

"There is but one way to find out which has the harder task," he said when he had listened to both of them, "and that is to exchange work. Let the tailor cry the news for a day, and the crier sew the seams. Then we shall see what we shall see."

The two friends were well pleased with

the parson's plan, and the very next morning
the crier took his place in the tailor's shop,
while the tailor went out with the crier's bell
to tell the news of a lost pig.

Ding-a-dong-ding! rang the bell, and the
tailor called as much like the
crier as he could: "Pig lost!
Pig lost! A white-and-
black pig! A pig with a
curly tail! A fat pig, a
small pig, a pig with four
legs!"

He called so loud
and so long that
when the pig was
discovered at last
in a garden not far
away, the tailor
was as hoarse as a
frog. But this made

no difference; before he had time to draw a long breath, he was sent to call the people to a town meeting. Then someone found a silk purse, and that must be told, though the purse was as empty as a last year's bird nest.

"A silk purse found! A silk purse found without a penny in it!" cried the poor tailor.

By and by he was forced to sit on a door-step to rest, but he had not been there long enough to clear his throat when here came the mayor to ask why he was idling away his time.

"Do you not know that a ship has come in with tea and spice from over the sea? Be up and off to tell the good news," said the mayor.

There was nothing for the tailor to do but to start out again, though his thoughts were whirling so fast in his head that he did not know what he was telling: "A spice has come in! A spice has come in! With a ship and a sea from over the tea," he sang in a sad voice.

This was news to make people wonder, you may be sure, and by the time the poor tailor had told them better he was ready to agree to anything the crier might say; and if he had but known it, the crier was as ready as he to own himself wrong.

— With prickles in his toes, cramps in his knees, and an ache in his back, the crier sat cross-legged in the tailor's warm corner wishing with all his heart that he were out in the wind and weather with his bell. The needle that he sewed with was bent, his thread was knotted, his fingers were all thumbs, and which was the front and which was the back of the coat he was to make for the mayor that day, he could not tell.

He turned the pieces this way and that, but when, at last,

he sewed them together, he was as uncertain as he had been in the beginning. He was about to put everything down and go to find the tailor, when he saw him staring in at the shop window and whining sadly: "A ship has come in with spices and tea."

"That is no way to tell news!" shouted the crier, shaking the shears at the tailor in his excitement. "Open your mouth like this and cry: *'A ship has come in! A ship has come in!'*"

The tailor opened his mouth so wide that the crier himself was surprised, but instead of the news of a ship he roared: *"The mayor's coat is spoiled! The armholes are sewed up! The pockets are upside down! The buttons are on the coat tails! The mayor's coat is spoiled!"*

All the while he was calling he rang the bell as if the town were on fire, and if the parson had not passed just then, there is no telling what might have happened next.

"There is but one thing to do," said the parson when he had heard all that there was to hear. "Each must take his old task again," and he would have said that there must be no more quarreling, but he had no time for this. No sooner had he spoken the words that set them free from their bargain than the tailor was inside his shop, and the crier was hurrying down the street making as much noise as if it were Christmas.

All over the town he could be heard ringing his bell and shouting joyfully: "Good news! Good news! A ship has come home! With spices and tea from over the sea, a ship has come home!"

There was no happier man anywhere than the town crier that day, unless it were the tailor as he sat in his cozy corner taking out every stitch that the crier had put in the mayor's coat.

Stop and Think

1. Describe the town crier's job.

2. What is a tailor's job?

3. Were the tailor and town crier content with their jobs at the beginning of the story? Why not?

4. Who gave the town crier and the tailor good advice? What was it?

Thankfulness

I thank Thee, Father, great and good,
    For this dear home so warm and bright;
I thank Thee for the sunny day,
    And for the sleepy, starry night.

I thank Thee for my father's arms,
    So big and strong, to hold me near;
I thank Thee for my mother's face,
    For brothers strong and sisters dear.

I thank Thee for the little birds
    That sing so sweetly in the trees;
I thank Thee for the rain and snow,
    And for the gentle evening breeze.

O Father, giver of all that's good,
    Hear my prayer today,
And hear the thanks I do not speak,
    The "Thank yous" I forget to say.

Word Watch

margarine	absolutely
imitating	peculiar
burglar	somersaults

The Lory Who Longed for Honey

ONCE upon a time, in a hot, sunny country, lived a very bright and beautiful parrot. He was red and green and gold and blue, with a dark purple top to his head. His real name was Lory. And he lived on honey.

There were hundreds of flowers growing among the trees, so all he had to do when he was hungry was to fly down and lick the honey out of the flowers. As a matter of fact, he had a tongue that was specially shaped for getting honey out of flowers. So he always had plenty to eat, and managed very well. And as long as he had plenty of honey, he was perfectly happy.

Then one day a sailor came to the forest looking for parrots. He found the parrot that liked honey and took him away. He didn't know that this parrot's real name was a Lory. He didn't know that he had a tongue specially shaped for getting honey out of flowers. He didn't even know he liked honey. He only knew he was a very bright and beautiful parrot and he meant to take him to England and sell him. So on board the ship he fed the parrot on sunflower seeds and taught him to

say: 'What have you got, what have you got, what have you got for me?' And whenever the Lory said this, the sailor gave him a sunflower seed. Although, as a matter of fact, he would very much rather have had honey.

When they reached England, the sailor sold the parrot who liked honey to an old lady who lived in a cottage on a hill. She didn't know much about parrots. She didn't know the parrot was a Lory. She didn't know he had a special tongue for licking honey out of flowers. She didn't even know he liked honey.

She called him Polly, and fed him on bits of bread and biscuit.

Now the old lady lived by herself and had to work very hard to make enough money to buy food. Generally she had just bread and margarine for tea, because she couldn't afford to buy honey even for herself, although she liked it.

Then one day when she wasn't in the least expecting it, the old lady's nephew who lived in South Africa sent her a present.

When the postman brought it, he said: 'Looks like a nice surprise, lady. Maybe some jam or some fruit.'

She carried the box carefully into her living room and unfastened it. It wasn't jam or fruit. It was six jars of honey all wrapped up in straw. Inside was a note which said:

> Dear Auntie,
>   I have managed to get a very nice job in South Africa, and I am making quite a bit of money. I am sure you are not able to buy all the things you need, so I am sending you six jars of honey. If you like them, I will send some more.
>   Love from your nephew,
>   Robert

The old lady was tremendously pleased and she took out the jars very carefully and put them in a row in the pantry. Then she cleared up all the straw and paper and string and said to herself: 'I'll start the first jar at teatime today.'

When the clock struck half-past three, the old lady put the kettle on the stove and began to cut some bread. It was certainly rather early for tea, but the old lady was so excited about the honey that she couldn't wait any longer. She put the bread and margarine on the table, took a plate and a knife, and a cup and saucer and spoon out of the cupboard, and then she went to the pantry.

All this made Polly very excited. He wasn't in his cage, but on a separate perch. The old lady let him sit here in the afternoons.

He could tell it was teatime, and when the old lady went to the pantry, he expected she would bring out some cake or fruit.

So he shouted at the top of his voice: 'What have you got, what have you got, what have you got for me?' When the old lady brought out neither cake nor fruit, but only a jar of yellow stuff, Polly was rather puzzled. But as soon as he saw her take some on her knife and spread the sticky stuff on her bread, and eat it with such pleasure, he knew it was honey.

And as soon as he knew it was honey, he knew he absolutely must think of some way of getting it for himself.

The old lady never dreamed of giving the Lory honey. She didn't know much about parrots.

But all the time the old lady was spreading the honey on her first slice of bread and thinking how wonderfully kind her nephew was to send it, and what an unexpected treat it was, the Lory was working out a plan.

Now parrots, as you know, are very clever at remembering words and also at imitating people, animals, and other sounds, and sometimes when they talk they can make their voice sound as if it is coming from a different part of the house altogether, so that you have no idea it is the parrot talking at all.

While the old lady was eating her bread and honey and enjoying it tremendously, she suddenly heard a *Meow!* It was really the Lory, but she didn't know that.

'There's a kitten outside,' she said. 'Poor thing, I expect it's lost. I'll let it in so that it can get warm by the fire.' And she went to the door and opened it.

Polly just had time to flutter on to the table and take a mouthful of honey with his special tongue and get on his perch again before she came back.

'How very strange,' she said, 'I'm sure I heard a kitten. Yet I've looked in the street, and there isn't a kitten to be seen.'

Polly winked and shouted: 'What have you got, what have you got, what have you got for me?' But the old lady still didn't know he was after the honey.

While the lady was spreading her *second*

slice of bread, he thought of another plan.
This time he made a noise like the kettle
boiling over.

'Goodness!' cried the old lady, jumping up.

And while she rushed out into the
kitchen, Polly flew down and took his second
big mouthful of honey.

'That's very peculiar,' said the old lady,
coming back again just as Polly scrambled on
to his perch. 'The kettle's perfectly all right,
and not boiling over at all.' But she still didn't
understand the Lory was after her honey.

Then he had what he thought was his
best plan of all. He made a noise like big
drops of rain falling on the roof.

'Oh heavens!' said the poor old lady. 'Now
I shall have to bring all the washing in.'

And she left her tea with the pot of honey
standing on the table, and went outside to
fetch in the washing before it got soaked.

She was a long time, because she had washed a tablecloth, two sheets, a pillowcase, a towel, a dress, a sweater, and the curtains from the bedroom. And while she was taking them all off the line, the Lory was swallowing honey as fast as he could.

At last, her arms full of washing, the old lady came back into the room. 'That's funny,' she said, as she looked at the window. 'The sun is shining as brightly as ever. I do believe I've brought all the washing in for nothing.'

'And that's funnier still!' she went on with a little scream, looking at the table. 'I do believe someone's been eating my honey!'

She picked up the jar and looked at it. There was just a scraping left at the bottom. Yet she had only opened the jar a few minutes ago.

'It must be a burglar,' she said, and feeling very brave she began to look under the

furniture and inside the cupboards and wherever a burglar might find space to hide.

All the time she was hunting, the Lory
was turning somersaults on his perch and
shrieking at the top of his voice: 'What have
you got, what have you got, what have you
got for me?'

When the old lady had decided there was
no burglar in the house, she went back to the
tea table.

And then she noticed drips of honey leading over the tablecloth, over the floor, and up to Polly's perch. She reached up and touched his perch, and, sure enough, that was sticky too.

'Why, you rascal!' she said. 'I do believe it was you who stole the honey.'

And that was how the old lady who didn't know much about parrots discovered that Lories like honey better than anything else in the world. After that, she always gave her Lory some honey for his tea, and she managed it quite well, because her nephew in South Africa sent her six jars every month.

But do you know, she never found out it was the Lory who played those tricks on her just to get a taste of her honey!

1. Who took the Lory away from his home in the forest?

2. What did the lady feed the Lory?

3. What surprise did the lady receive in the mail one day?

4. What three tricks did the Lory play on the lady to get her to leave the room?

5. How did the lady react each time she heard these noises? What did the Lory do?

nought: nothing

Some One

Some one came knocking
    At my wee, small door;
Some one came knocking,
    I'm sure—sure—sure;
I listened, I opened,
    I looked to left and right,
But nought there was a-stirring
    In the still dark night;
Only the busy beetle
    Tap-tapping in the wall,
Only from the forest
    The screech-owl's call,
Only the cricket whistling
    While the dewdrops fall,
So I know not who came knocking,
    At all, at all, at all.

—*Walter de la Mare*

Greedy Greta

Once upon a time there lived a little girl named Greta. One day Greta went to the grocery store with her Grandmother Grace. Grandmother Grace said, as she backed her green car out of the garage, "Greta, if you are a good girl at the grocery store, I will get you a great gift."

While Grandmother Grace was getting her groceries, Greta greeted everyone that she met saying, "Grandmother Grace is going to get me a great gift if I am a good girl!" Grandmother got some grapes, grapefruit, goulash, and garlic. She bought a gallon of milk, whole-grain bread, and garden green beans.

Well, all the time Grandmother Grace shopped, Greta was as good as gold, and Grandmother Grace did get her a good gift. Grandmother hid the gift behind her back, and said, "Guess, Greta, guess." And to help Greta, Grandmother gave Greta a poem puzzle clue. She said about the gift:

> Its two words are easy:
> The first rhymes with 'gurple'
> Begins with a 'p'
> Its a color called p_____ .
> The second's a word
> That rhymes with 'glum.'
> It's sticky and chewy
> And gooey; it's _____.

Giggling Greta guessed it right off!! "Purple Gum! Purple Grape Gum!" she shouted with glee, as she grabbed and gobbled the first glob. "I'm so grateful you gave me this good gift," Greta chewed and gabbed in a garbled way. As Greta gleefully chewed the gooey grape gum, she chattered away to her grandmother: "I sure am glad that my sister, Gertie, and my brother, Gilbert, didn't come with us to the grocery store, because they might have gotten some of my grape gum."

Then, in the midst of Greta's glee, Greta stood very still. Grandmother Grace was giving Greta the serious, well-known, straight-in-the-eye glance. This glance meant "Stop! Be quiet, sweet Greta! Listen!" Greta froze where she stood to hear the great, quiet voice of her Grandmother Grace. And as her grandmother spoke, Greta's glamorous grin turned into a grouchy grump, a frown and a half. "Sweet Greta," Grandmother said with her loving arm around Greta, "when we get home, I want you to be a good girl and give some of your grape gum to Gertie and Gilbert."

When Greta heard what her Grandmother Grace asked, Greta frowned. Greta pouted. Greta got grumpier and grumpier the more she thought about sharing the grape gum. Greta glumly sat in the back seat all the way home to Greenville. Finally Greta growled to Grandmother Grace, "I don't WANT to give any of my grape gum to Gertie and Gilbert. I want this gum to be all mine because you gave it to me for being a good girl." Greta grumbled and growled and then grumbled and growled some more. Suddenly, Greta had a great, greedy idea. "I'll gobble the grape gum until it is all gone. Then I won't have to give any to Gertie and

Gilbert," gasped Greta to herself. And that's exactly what greedy Greta did. Greedy Greta gobbled great gobs of gooey grape gum. Suddenly, Greta gulped! Greta gasped! Greta grew ghastly green. Greta greatly regretted the greedy gain that she had gotten.

When Grandmother Grace and Greta got home, they saw Gertie and Gilbert going to a golf game with their Grandfather Guy. "Come on, Greta; let's go to the golf game," grinned Grandfather Guy.

But Greta groaned, "Go without me, Grandfather; I feel too ghastly to go anywhere." Greedy Greta said on her way to bed, "I'll never, never be greedy again. I have learned that grabbing and gobbling are ungodly. From now on, I will give to Gertie and Gilbert." And to this day, Greta always gives her goodies to Gertie and Gilbert, and they always give to Greta.

As Grandfather Guy grabbed the doorknob to leave, he gave her a gem of love to remember. Grandfather called, "Goodbye, goodly Greta. You are truly a *grand* granddaughter." And from those words from her grandfather, Greta gained another gift. Greta gained a gift greater by far than gum. What could be greater than gum? She gained the glorious gift of her grandfather's grin. To this very day, his smile lives in Greta's memory, even though she is all grown up and still *gives* happily ever after.

 Stop and Think

1. Who went shopping at the grocery store?

2. What did Greta have to do to take home a great gift?

3. What was Greta's gift?

4. How did Greta react when Grandma told her she must share her gum with her brother and sister?

5. What lesson did Greta learn?

 **The Bible Says,**

"And as ye would that men should do to you, do ye also to them likewise."

Luke 6:31

withered   cruse   morsel

The Woman Who Shared Her Last Loaf

from 1 Kings 17

In Israel and the nearby lands, no rain had fallen for many months. The grass and flowers were withered, the fruit trees were dead, the grain fields and gardens were empty, and the streams were almost dried up.

In the time of this fearful famine, a poor woman looked into her jar of flour and cruse of oil and saw that they were almost empty. She said, "There is just enough flour to make one more little cake, and just enough oil to mix it. I will go and gather a few sticks and bake this little cake for my boy and myself, and we will eat it and die."

As she was out gathering the sticks, she heard someone speak. She looked up and saw a strange man standing near. He was tired and worn and dusty, as though he had been walking many miles in the hot sun. He said to her, "Fetch me, I pray you, a little water, that I may drink."

She forgot for a moment how hungry and sad she was and started at once toward her house to get the water for him. As she was going, he called to her, "Bring me, I pray you,

a morsel of bread in your hand."

She turned back with a sigh and said, "O sir, truly I have not a cake; I have only a handful of meal in the jar, and a little oil in the cruse, and now I am gathering two sticks that I may go in and prepare it for me and my boy that we may eat it and die."

The man said, "Fear not; go and do as you have said, but make me a little cake first, and bring it out here to me, and afterward make a cake for yourself and your boy. For Jehovah, the God of Israel, says, 'The jar of meal shall not be empty, neither shall the little bottle of oil be empty, until it rains upon the earth.' "

She stood and looked at this strange man with his strange request—to share her very last piece of bread. She did not know who he was, nor who the God was he spoke of. She only knew that this man with the tired face was hungry too, and did not have even one piece of bread, and she said to herself, "I will share what we have with him."

She went back into her kitchen and started the fire with the sticks. She scraped the last bit of flour from the jar into the pan and poured in the last drop of oil from the cruse. Then she looked into the jar and cruse and saw that there was just as much flour

and oil as before! She made the cake and took it to Elijah, God's prophet. She, Elijah, and her son had enough food from the jar of meal that did

not empty and the cruse of oil that did not fail to last all the days of that famine. And it all came about because that good woman,

though hungry herself, was willing to share the little she had with another who was in need.

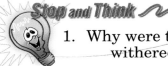

Stop and Think

1. Why were the fields and gardens all withered and dried up?

2. Who did Elijah ask for something to eat?

3. What did Elijah promise would happen if the poor woman fed him first?

4. What happened when the poor woman believed Elijah and did what he asked?

The Bible Says,

"Give, and it shall be given unto you; good measure, pressed down, and shaken together, and running over."

Luke 6:38a

Missionary Penny

One day a girl named Mary went to Sunday school. The teacher told the class about a missionary box that was to be sent to Africa. Everyone was to bring something. Some of the children suggested the things they could bring, such as combs, towels, and soap, but Mary was poor and didn't have anything to bring. She went home and prayed about it. Then she forgot about it, because she believed God would answer her prayers.

The next day while Mary was out playing, she happened to see a penny on the ground.

She was very happy, because she hadn't had as much as a penny in a long time. She began thinking of the things it would buy—candy, gum, a small toy. (Many years ago when this story took place, a penny could buy all of these things!) Then, remembering her prayer, she decided to save it and take it to Sunday school.

That Sunday, after the other children had gone, Mary asked the teacher what a penny would buy for the missionary box. The teacher was about to say that it wouldn't buy anything, but she looked at Mary's ragged clothes and thought carefully for a minute.

"Why, Mary!" she exclaimed. "It would buy a gospel tract!"

The teacher wrote the missionary a letter telling her about Mary and asking her to pray before she gave the tract to anyone.

The missionary kept the tract for many months, praying about how to use it. Then one day an African chief, the chief of a village some distance away, came to the mission compound. When she saw him, something impressed her that he was the one who should have the tract.

He took it to his village, reading it three times. He could not sleep that night nor eat his breakfast the next morning, so he decided to take the tract back to the missionary.

"I do not want it," he said to the missionary. "It makes me feel bad inside."

"That is God's Word speaking to you," the missionary explained.

"God is telling you that you have done bad things and need to accept Christ as your Savior." Then she carefully explained to the chief the way of salvation. There and then the chief accepted Christ and was saved and went on his way home rejoicing.

About a year afterwards, the missionary decided to visit the chief's village and see if he had really been saved. To her great surprise, she found a church in the village. The missionary learned that when the chief went home from the mission compound, he started gathering his people together every night after they came in from work. He read the tract to them and gave his testimony of how he had been saved. As a result of such witnessing, 1,500 people had come to accept Christ as their Savior.

Just think, this wonderful thing happened

all because Mary gave her all to Jesus! What can you give Him today? And whom can you tell about His love? It does not have to be someone across the seas. It could be someone right in your own town.

Stop and Think

1. What had the teacher asked the children to bring to Sunday school?

2. Why was it a sacrifice for Mary to give her penny for the missionary box?

3. What did the teacher say her penny could buy?

4. Who did the missionary give the tract to?

5. What happened because of Mary's gospel tract?

Prayer of a Child

The Shepherds had an Angel,
    The Wise Men had a star,
But what have I, a little child,
    To guide me home from far,
Where glad stars sing together
    And singing angels are?—

The Wise Men left their country
    To journey morn by morn,
With gold and frankincense and myrrh,
    Because the Lord was born:
God sent a star to guide them
    And sent a dream to warn.

My life is like their journey,
    Their star is like God's book;
I must be like those good Wise Men
    With heavenward heart and look:
But shall I give no gifts to God?—
    What precious gifts they took!

Lord, I will give my love to Thee,
    Than gold much costlier,
Sweeter to Thee than frankincense,
    More prized than choicest myrrh:
Lord, make me dearer day by day,
    Day by day holier.

—*Christina Rossetti*

Black Beauty's First Home

This story is told by a beautiful black horse. It is the first chapter in the book, *Black Beauty*. The book is filled with good lessons; you will want to read it.

The first place that I can well remember was a large, pleasant meadow with a pond of clear water in it. Some shady trees leaned over it, and rushes and water lilies grew at the deep end.

Over the hedge on one side we looked into a plowed field, and on the other we looked over a gate at our master's house, which stood by the roadside. At the top of the meadow was a grove of trees, and at the bottom a running brook overhung by a steep bank.

While I was young, I lived on my mother's milk, as I could not eat grass. In the daytime I ran by her side, and at night I lay down close by her. When it was hot, we used to stand by the pond in the shade of the trees, and when it was cold, we had a nice, warm shed near the grove.

As soon as I was old enough to eat grass, my mother used to go out to work in the daytime, and come back in the evening.

There were six colts in the meadow besides me; they were older than I was; some were nearly as large as grown-up horses. We used to gallop all together round and round the field as hard as we could go. Sometimes we had rather rough play, for they would often bite and kick as well as gallop.

One day when there was a great deal of kicking, my mother called me to come to her, and then she said, "I wish you to pay attention to what I am going to say to you. Your grandmother had manners and the sweetest temper of any horse I ever knew, and I think you have never seen me kick or bite.

"I hope you will grow up gentle and good, and never learn bad ways. Do your work with a good will, lift your feet up well when you trot, and never bite or kick even in play."

I have never forgotten my mother's advice. I knew she was a wise old horse, and our master thought a great deal of her, and called her Pet.

Our master was a good, kind man. He gave us good food, good lodging, and kind words; he spoke as kindly to us as he did to his children. We were all fond of him, and my mother loved him very much. When she saw him at the gate, she would neigh with joy, and trot up to him. He would pat and stroke her, and say, "Well, old Pet, and how is your little one?"

He would give me a piece of bread, which was very good, and sometimes he brought a carrot for my mother. All the horses would come to him, but I think we were his favorites. My mother always took him to the town on market day in a light wagon.

There was a boy named Dick who sometimes came into our field to gather blackberries. When he had eaten all he wanted, he would have, what he called, fun with the colts, throwing stones and sticks at them to make them gallop.

We did not mind him much, for we could gallop off; but sometimes a stone would hit and hurt us.

One day he was at this game, and did not know that the master was in the next field. But he was there, watching what was going on. Soon over the hedge he jumped, and catching Dick by the arm, he gave him such a shaking that we could hear him roar with the pain and surprise.

As soon as we saw the master, we trotted up nearer to see what went on.

"Bad boy!" he said, "bad boy! to chase the colts. This is not the first time, nor the second, but it shall be the last. There—take your money and go home; I shall not want you on my farm again."

So we never saw Dick any more. Old Daniel, the man who looked after the horses, was just as gentle as our master, so we were well off.

Stop and Think

1. Describe Black Beauty's first home.

2. What did Black Beauty's mother think of rough play?

3. Who were the master's favorite horses?

4. Why was Dick told not to come back to the meadow again?

Word
Watch

Eddie Rickenbacker

(ĕd′die rĭck′ən·băck·ər)

baby carriage   pushmobile

ball-bearing wheels

Built for Speed

Eddie Rickenbacker's father stood with his eyes fixed on his son in a stony stare.

Eddie faced his angry father fearfully. "But I didn't touch Mrs. Clancy's baby. I didn't even know the baby was there."

"You heard Mrs. Clancy calling!" Eddie's father roared. "Why didn't you stop? Why did you want Mrs. Clancy's baby carriage anyway?"

"I didn't want her baby carriage," answered Eddie, "or her baby either."

"You didn't want it!" Mr. Rickenbacker shouted. "You saw Mrs. Clancy's carriage in her yard. You pushed it up the street as fast as you could run! And now you tell me you didn't want it! Then tell me, why did you take it?"

Eddie knew that he was going to have a very hard time making his father understand what he had just done. It was the quickest way to find out what he needed to know if he were going to win the race next week.

"Well, Father," he said, "I've been watching those new baby carriages. Their wheels seem to turn faster than the old kind."

"What do you care?" his father asked. "We're not going to get one."

"I know. But we're having a pushmobile race next week. I think I can win it if I have some wheels like the wheels on Mrs. Clancy's baby carriage."

"So! You thought—" Mr. Rickenbacker began. But Eddie stopped him.

"No! I didn't! I just wanted to find out what made Mrs. Clancy's carriage easier to push than ours. It was a trial run."

Eddie's father had always been glad that Eddie had an interest in learning how things worked. So now he asked, "Did you find out?"

"Yes," said Eddie quickly. "Those wheels have little balls of steel inside them that roll around when they turn, and it makes them run a lot faster."

"Balls of steel!" exclaimed Mr. Rickenbacker.

"Yes. They're called ball-bearing wheels. And I'm sure if my pushmobile had wheels like those on Mrs. Clancy's baby carriage, I could win the pushmobile race next week."

"Pushmobile races! That's all you boys think about!" said Mr. Rickenbacker. "Why don't you do some work for a change?"

"We *do* work. We worked hard to get the track ready," answered Eddie. "This will be the best race we've ever had."

Mr. Rickenbacker turned. "Well, don't let me hear of your using any baby carriage for another trial run," he said, and he walked up the path.

As soon as his father had gone, Eddie's thoughts jumped back to his beautiful, bright yellow soap box. Painted on it, in big green letters, was MILE-A-MINUTE-MURPHY.

Everything was ready now, that is, everything except the wheels.

"Somewhere, somehow, I just *have* to find some ball-bearing wheels," Eddie said.

Eddie could almost see MILE-A-MINUTE-MURPHY whizzing past the finish line. He was thinking so hard that he didn't notice the bumping of wagon wheels and the sound of a horse coming up the road.

It was old Sam, making his rounds with his scrap wagon.

"Any old clothes? Any old papers?" Sam called.

"No. None today," said Eddie. But then, at the sight of the loaded wagon, he whirled about and ran calling, "Wait, Sam! Wait!"

Sam drew his horse to a stop and waited.

"Sam, do you have any old wheels off a baby carriage?" Eddie asked breathlessly.

"Why, yes," answered Sam. "I think I have one or two pairs."

With one jump, Eddie was in the wagon.

Yes, there were the wheels! He grabbed them up, one by one, and whirled them around in the air. Sam stared at him, wide-eyed.

Eddie's face fell, and he tossed the wheels down again. There wasn't one ball-bearing wheel among them.

"What's the matter?" Sam asked.

"Don't those wheels turn all right?"

"Oh, yes, they turn all right," answered Eddie. "But I have to have the new kind, with ball bearings." Then he told Sam how he planned to use the carriage wheels to win the pushmobile race.

"I'll look, Eddie," offered Sam. "Maybe I can find some for you."

Eddie had little hope that Sam could help. Ball-bearing wheels were still too new. Not many people would be selling a new baby carriage.

Eddie was disappointed, but he felt certain that if he just kept on trying, somehow things would turn out right. "Never give up," he told himself.

He started for town. He walked up one street and down the other, looking in all the secondhand stores. But not one ball-bearing wheel could he find.

As the day of the big race drew nearer and nearer, Eddie began to get discouraged. He kept reminding himself that he shouldn't

give up. That was certainly no way to become a winner.

Finally the day before the race arrived. Eddie went around to all the secondhand stores once more, but it was no use. Not one baby carriage with ball-bearing wheels had come in since he first started looking.

Late that afternoon, Eddie turned in at the gate of the Rickenbacker home. He was just going to be forced to put the same old wheels back on MILE-A-MINUTE-MURPHY.

Suddenly he heard Sam's voice calling, "Eddie! Eddie!"

Eddie whirled about and ran toward the gate. "Did you get them?" he shouted as Sam pulled at the horse's reins.

Sam's friendly smile was enough of a reply for Eddie. He was in the wagon with one big jump. There, at last, were two pairs of just the kind of ball-bearing wheels that Eddie had been looking for.

The crowd gathered early at the race track the next day.

All of the brightly painted pushmobiles were there, ready to go. The drivers climbed into their places and picked up their steering ropes. Then the pushers took their places behind.

Eddie knew he had picked the fastest runner on his block for his pusher. He turned and winked at him now. Only the two of them knew the secret of the four ball-bearing wheels. MILE-A-MINUTE-MURPHY was all ready to go.

The starter raised his arm. "Stay be-tween your lines, boys!" he shouted. "And don't try to trip the pushers! Now ready, set, *GO!*"

The crowd roared, and the pushmobiles were off!

Drivers and pushers called to each other through clouds of dust.

Eddie held his steering rope tightly in his hands. Out of the corner of his eye, he saw that several pushmobiles had piled up on top of each other. But MILE-A-MINUTE-MURPHY whizzed on with its ball-bearing wheels fairly flying.

Just as Eddie had dreamed, MILE-A-MINUTE-MURPHY tore past the finish line with the other pushmobiles all trailing behind.

Eddie jumped out of his soap box and hugged his pusher. His friends came running up. They pounded Eddie and his pusher on their backs, shouting, "You've won! You've won!"

Eddie was grinning happily. Then he turned and pushed his way through the crowd to where his father was standing.

"It was those ball-bearing wheels that did it, Father," he said.

Mr. Rickenbacker laid his arm across Eddie's shoulder and chuckled.

"Don't you think you should give half of the prize to Mrs. Clancy? After all, it was her baby carriage you used for a trial run!"

Eddie Rickenbacker himself was "built for speed." When he grew up, he learned to fly. In World War I, he shot down more enemy planes than any other flier. The boy who wanted to be a winner became a man who helped his country to win a war.

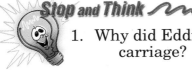

Stop and Think

1. Why did Eddie take Mrs. Clancy's baby carriage?

2. What made the new wheels better than the old wheels?

3. What was the name of Eddie's pushmobile?

4. Why do you think they called it a *pushmobile?*

5. How did Eddie show that he wasn't a quitter?

Charlestown	gunpowder
shadowy	courthouse
stirrup	powder

The Ride of Paul Revere

Shall I tell you about the midnight ride of Paul Revere? It happened a long time ago when this country was ruled by the king of England.

The king had sent British soldiers to Boston to guard the streets of the town and make sure that no one went out or came in without their permission.

The people did not like to be treated in this way. They said, "Shall we allow our liberties to be taken from us? Shall we give up all the rights that are so dear to us?"

The whole country was stirred up. Brave men left their homes and hurried toward Boston to give the people there whatever help they could.

"We do not want to fight against the king," they said; "but we must defend ourselves and our friends from those soldiers of his. We are free men, and he must not take away our liberties."

Some of them gathered at Charlestown, just across the river from Boston, and from there they watched to see what the soldiers would do.

At Concord, eighteen miles away, these men had stored some gunpowder. When the British soldiers heard of it, they made up their minds to go out and get it for themselves or destroy it.

Among the watchers at Charlestown was a brave young man named Paul Revere. A friend of his, who lived in Boston, came across the river one day to see him.

"I have something to tell you," he said. "The British are going to Concord to destroy the powder that is there. Indeed, they are getting ready to go this very night."

"Very well," said Paul Revere. "They will find that we are not all asleep. As soon as they are ready to start, you must let me know. Hang a lantern in the tower of the old North Church. If they are coming straight across the river, hang two. I will be here, ready. The moment I see the light, I will mount my horse and ride to Concord to spread the alarm."

And so it was done. Hour after hour that night, Paul Revere waited and watched by the side of the river. He walked up and down the bank, leading his horse behind him. He kept his eyes turned always toward Boston.

The town was dark and still. By the dim light of the moon he could see the shadowy form of the old North Church. Now and then he could hear the call of some soldier on guard or the bark of a dog far away. He heard the clock strike nine, then ten, then eleven. "Perhaps they will not go tonight," he said to himself.

But just as he spoke, he saw a light shine out from the tower of the church. "Ah! at last!" he cried. He spoke to his horse. He put his foot in the stirrup. He waited one moment. Then, clear and bright, another light flashed from the tower. The soldiers were coming straight across the river!

He sprang into the saddle. Like an arrow from the bow, his horse leaped forward. Away they went. Through the village street, and out upon the country road, they flew like the wind. "Up! up!" cried Paul Revere. "The soldiers are coming! Up! up! and defend your homes!"

The cry awoke the farmers from their sleep. They sprang from their beds and looked out. They could not see the swift horse speeding away toward Concord, but they heard the clatter of hoofs far down the road; they heard the cry again: "Up! up! The British!"

"It is the alarm!" they cried. "The redcoats are coming." And they took up their guns, their axes—

anything they could find—and hurried out to help their friends drive back the British.

So through the night Paul Revere rode on toward Concord. At every farmhouse and in every village he gave the cry of alarm. It was not a cry of fear. It was the cry which called brave men to their duty. The alarm was spread. Guns were fired. Bells were rung. Everybody was aroused.

The British soldiers went on to Concord as they had planned. On the way, they met and killed some of the brave men who had come out to defend their homes. They burned the courthouse at Concord. They destroyed what they could find.

But they were not to return so easily. It seemed as though every man in the country was after them. There was fighting all along the road. The farmers from behind the fences and walls shot the red-coated soldiers down

as they passed. Those who escaped were glad
enough when they found themselves safe in
Boston once more.

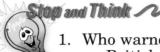

Stop and Think

1. Who warned Paul Revere that the British were going to Concord to destroy the gunpowder there?

2. What was the signal that the soldiers were coming across the river and going to Concord?

3. How did Paul Revere warn people that the British were coming?

Word Watch

| intense | chamber |
| lodger | hastened |

How Lydia Darrah Served Her Country

LYDIA DARRAH, a young Quaker woman, was sitting by her fireside, in Philadelphia, one bitter cold afternoon in December, 1777.

Lydia Darrah longed to serve her country. While she looked out of her window this snowy afternoon she was thinking of Washington and his army shivering at Whitemarsh.

There had been intense fighting about Philadelphia and the patriots were having a hard time. And now Washington and men were suffering many hardships in camp, while General Howe, the British commander, was wintering his men in Philadelphia in ease and luxury.

One of General Howe's chief officers had rented rooms of Lydia Darrah. Since the house was in a quiet spot it soon became a favorite place for British officers to meet and talk over their plans.

"Mistress Lydia," the British officer had said to her one morning, "I expect some friends here tonight; I want you to have the back room upstairs ready. And as they are likely to stay late, be sure and see that your folks are in bed at an early hour.

"When my friends are ready to go," continued the officer, "I will call you, that you may let them out and put out the fire and the candles."

"It shall be done as thee orders," quietly said the young Quaker woman.

Sure enough, several of Howe's chief officers came to the house that evening as if on important business. The family were all in bed except Lydia, who sat up to open the door.

"You may go to bed now, Mistress Lydia," said the officer, "and I will rap on your door when my guests are ready to go."

Lydia went to her room and lay down without undressing. She was restless and could not sleep.

"What were those officers talking about?" she thought. "Why did they have this secret meeting at her house? Didn't it mean harm to Washington and his army?"

All these things came rushing into her mind as she lay there wide awake.

All of a sudden Lydia slid from her bed and stole from her room in stocking feet.

Still as a mouse she crept down the hall to the door of the officer's chamber. She put her ear to the key-hole and listened.

What did she hear?

It was the voice of her lodger reading aloud an order from Sir William Howe.

"Tomorrow night," the officer read, "the troops will secretly leave the city and march out to attack and capture, if possible, the American army at Whitemarsh."

Lydia had heard enough. With her heart beating fast she softly made her way back to bed, but not to sleep.

An hour went by.

Rap! rap!

It was a knock at her door. The officers were ready to go home.

Rap! rap! louder than before.

"How soundly that young woman sleeps!" muttered the British officer.

Rap! rap! rap!

This time the knocking was loud and sharp.

"I shall be ready in a moment," answered a sleepy voice.

Lydia opened the street door for her midnight callers, then put out the lights and the fires and went back to bed.

Not a wink of sleep for her the rest of the night. She had now in her keeping a great secret.

What should she do? How should she warn General Washington of his peril?

As she thought over her plans the good woman prayed that God might help her in what she hoped to do.

Long before daybreak she got up. She told her husband that the flour was out and she must go over to the mill at Frankfort to get some.

"Yes," said the good man; "but thee must take a servant for company."

But Lydia went alone.

Bright and early Lydia started for General Howe's headquarters to ask permission to go through the British lines. She easily got her pass and at once set out on her long walk through the snow. The flour mill was nearly five miles away.

Leaving her bag at the mill, she hurried on to the American outposts. There she was stopped by a sentinel and taken before Colonel Craig, the commander. She told him her story.

When she had finished she begged him to keep her name a secret and hastened back to the mill. Then, with the bag of flour over her shoulder, she made her way back to town.

It was so early that nobody had noticed her absence.

Thursday evening after dark the whole British force left Philadelphia. From her window Lydia Darrah saw the long line of redcoats and heard the sharp commands of the officers as the army marched quickly by.

"Has Washington received my message? Will he be on his guard?" she said to herself.

At daybreak Friday, when the British drew near Whitemarsh, the patriot army was seen drawn up in line of battle. Lydia's message had reached headquarters and Washington was ready to fight.

General Howe had respect for Washington's skill as a soldier, and so did not dare make the attack. There was, however, a good deal of marching to and fro and some fighting.

"On the following Monday," wrote Washington to Congress, "the British left very hastily and marched back to Philadelphia."

It was a nice little trap that General Howe had set, but Washington acted too quickly to be caught.

But how about the meek little Quaker woman? Would anybody think it was she who spoiled the plans of the British commander?

"Come to my room, Mistress Lydia; I want to ask you something," said the redcoat lodger the morning after his return.

With fear she obeyed.

"Were any of your family up," asked the officer, "on the night I had company in my room?"

"No, indeed, sir," replied Lydia; "they were all in bed at eight o'clock, just as I was bidden by thee."

The officer seemed puzzled. He looked long and hard at Lydia's calm face.

"It is strange," he said; "and yet you were sound asleep, for I rapped on your door three times before you heard me. In some way or another Washington, the sly old fox, got wind of our plan. He was ready for us, and all we could do was to march back to town like a pack of fools."

The British continued their merry life that winter in Philadelphia, while the patriot army, after leaving Whitemarsh, lay shoeless and half starved in the camp at Valley Forge.

It was long after the war for our independence was over before Lydia Darrah's secret was told.

Stop and Think

1. Who rented a room from Lydia Darrah?

2. What did the British officers often use her house for?

3. What did Lydia do one night while the officers were meeting?

4. What British plan did Lydia overhear?

5. How did Lydia get news to General Washington of the British attack?

6. What happened when the British got to Whitemarsh to attack the American army?

America, Our Country

America, our country,
Has half a continent,
An ocean for the sun to rise
And one for its descent.
And space for many children
Of different speech and ways,
But standing as one people
In strength and love and praise.

—*Dorothy Hall*

noble   cruelly   regret

Nathan Hale

In the roll of our country's heroes, no name shines brighter than that of Nathan Hale. This noble young soldier was a captain in the American army at a time when we were at war with the English.

George Washington, the leader of the American armies, wanted to find out the plans of the English army and learn just how strong it was. Nathan Hale, feeling that it was his duty to do all he could for his native land, offered to go into the enemy's camp and discover the things that General Washington wanted to know.

Taking off his captain's uniform and disguising himself as well as he could, this brave young man crossed over to Long Island and made his way into the middle of the English camp. He looked at all their forts and made drawings of them and learned much about what the English commander, General Howe, was thinking of doing.

He then started to return, but he was taken prisoner and carried before the English general. When Hale saw that his purpose was known, he frankly told who he was and what he had come for, and General Howe ordered him to be hanged as a spy.

But was he a spy? When we speak of a spy, we think of one who, for pay, enters the camp of an enemy to learn his secrets. In this meaning Nathan Hale was no spy. For, why did he offer himself for this service? For pay? No! for duty—for love of his country.

The order of the English general was carried out the next morning, and poor Hale was treated most cruelly. Every favor was denied him. General Howe would not permit the young American to see a pastor, nor even to have a Bible.

But a high and holy feeling upheld the brave youth in his last hour. With almost joyous step he walked to the place of death, and with his last breath spoke these words— words that will never die: "I only regret that I have but one life to lose for my country."

Stop and Think

1. With whom were the Americans at war when this story took place?

2. What did Nathan Hale volunteer to do?

3. What happened to Nathan Hale?

Word Watch

might and main: strength and power

Washington and His Hatchet

The story of George Washington cutting down the cherry tree is a legend, but it does tell us about his reputation for honesty.

He had a hatchet—little George—
    A hatchet bright and new,
And sharp enough to cut a stick—
    A little stick—in two.

He hacked and whacked and
        whacked and hacked,
    This sturdy little man;
He hacked a log and hacked a fence,
    As round about he ran.

He hacked his father's cherry tree
And made an ugly spot;
The bark was soft, the hatchet sharp.
And little George forgot.

You know the rest. The father frowned
And asked the reason why;
You know the good old story runs:
He could not tell a lie.

The boy that chopped that cherry tree
Soon grew to be a youth;
At work and books he hacked away,
And still he told the truth.

The youth became a famous man,
Above six feet in height,
And when he had good work to do,
He hacked with all his might.

He fought the armies that the king
Had sent across the sea;
He battled up and down the land
To set his country free.

For seven long years he hacked and whacked
With all his might and main,
Until the British sailed away
And did not come again.

—*Edward Eggleston*

Word Watch

exaggerating   enormous

diddled   dreadfully

uncomfortable   St. Bernard

importantly   reluctantly

Whopper

Whopper Mason was trotting home as fast as his two short legs could carry him. A thin trickle of blood dropped from his nose.

"Boy, oh, boy," he chanted aloud to himself, "was that a fight!" He doubled up his fists and pretended to down an enemy. "Boy, oh, boy, I certainly had him on the run!"

A boy stood suddenly in his path, a bigger boy than Whopper. "Hi, Whopper," he said. "Where'd you get the nose?"

Whopper kept on poking his fists at thin air. "Fighting," he answered excitedly. "Boy, was that a fight! First I sock him, and then

he socks me, and then I sock him, and then . . ."

"Who?" said the big boy.

"Willie Taylor. And then he socks me, and . . ."

"Willie Taylor isn't allowed to fight. His mother won't like it a bit when I tell her."

Some of the punch went out of Whopper then. His fists poked feebly, and then fell to his sides. He wiped at his nose with his handkerchief.

"Oh," he said. "Isn't he? Well," he admitted. "He wasn't really fighting, Jess. I just took a poke at him, and . . . and. . . ."

"And what?" said Jess.

"And I swung so hard I fell down," Whopper confessed. "And that's what happened to my nose."

"That's what I thought," Jess said. "Whopper Mason, when are you going to quit making up those big stories? If you'd kept on with this one, you'd have gotten Willie in trouble."

Whopper kicked at the dirt with his toe. "Well, I guess I'm *trying*, Jess," he said. "Only sometimes I forget."

He went on his way, very depressed. Telling big stories, Jess called it. Ex-ag-ger-ating, his parents said. But to Whopper, it was only making dull things exciting. Nevertheless, he was going to stop it, just as he'd promised Jess.

Whopper ran into the house and got his new police car. Playing with the car always cheered him up. First he built ramps from

couch pillows and pieces he had torn from cardboard boxes. Soon he was in the midst of a terrific police chase. The police car was just about to go over the ramp, closing in on the enemy, when the little boy from next door came over to watch. Whopper sent him home again for fear he'd get in the way. The police car had just made a glorious landing when Whopper saw the man.

He was a big man, at least to Whopper's eyes, with a mustache and a cane. He was talking to the little boy next door. Whopper went back to his police chase, but he did notice the little boy walking away with the man presently.

The police had just "gotten their man," and Whopper was picking up the pieces when he felt a hand shaking his shoulder. It was the mother of the little boy next door. "Whopper," she was asking anxiously, "have you seen Petie?"

"Oh, sure," Whopper answered. "A man took him away."

Petie's mother looked still more anxious. "A man?" she cried. "What did he look like?"

Whopper felt the pleasant glow of creation spreading within him. "Oh, an enormous man," he recited happily. "Just *enormous!* Like the fellows Popeye knocks out. And his face was all hairy . . . big black beard 'n everything. And he had a great big stick in his hand. . . ."

Petie's mother was looking scared. "Oh, my goodness," she said over and over, running to her house. "Oh, my goodness!"

Whopper felt quite pleased with himself. He went in for a drink. That really had been an exciting story. But then, Whopper's heart sank. Hadn't that been ex-ag-ger-ating? Anyway, a little? He thought of Jess and squirmed.

He diddled a little longer over his drink, but his way was plain before him. Slowly, slowly, he went across the lawn to Petie's home. The yard was filled with people, all talking loudly. But Whopper hardly saw them. He singled out Petie's mother.

"Say," he said, feeling dreadfully uncomfortable. "Say, that fellow that walked away with Petie . . . he wasn't so big, not so awfully big." A silence fell on the group of people. Still Whopper didn't notice. He was too busy trying to describe the stranger exactly.

"And he didn't have a beard," he went on, "just a little teeny black mustache. And he carried a cane, not a stick."

Petie's mother dropped limply down on the porch steps. "Why, that was John," she cried, "Petie's Uncle John. And I thought Petie'd been kidnapped!" She whirled suddenly on Whopper. "Whopper Mason!" she began severely.

Fifteen minutes later, Whopper was still trying to forget what she and everybody else

had said. You would think they'd rather
Petie'd been kidnapped than have been
scared for nothing. A fine lot of good it did a
person to tell the truth. Though, he admitted
honestly, if he'd told the exact truth *first,*
nobody would have been scared.

Whopper had two pennies in his pocket,
and he was going to spend them. He felt the
need of a couple of good suckers. Orange, he
thought.

"Rrrruff!" something said at his heels.
Whopper jumped. A little black Scotty had
whirled out of the bushes, and was barking at
his shoes.

"Whoa!" Whopper said, moving ahead at
a fast clip. A backward look told him the
Scotty wasn't following. His dragging leash
seemed tangled in the bushes. But Whopper
wasn't taking any chances on its getting

*un*tangled. He kept on running all the way to the drugstore.

"Whew!" he gasped, bursting in the door. "Was I ever scared!"

A man phoning at the far end of the counter frowned at him. Whopper lowered his voice politely, but his excitement rose high.

"A big dog chased me!" he told the drugstore man importantly. "A great, big barking dog. Must have been a St. Bernard or something!"

"St. Bernards are friendly," the drugstore man said. "Could it have been a police dog?"

"Must have been," Whopper cried happily.

"Chased me for blocks. I tried to climb a tree, and it pulled me down, and I just barely got over a fence. . . ."

His high spirits suddenly faded. He was remembering Jess. Slowly, his shoulders sagged.

"No," he admitted. "It wasn't a police dog." The scene at Petie's house came back to him. Maybe he'd just not explain things any further. But Jess wouldn't like that.

Reluctantly, Whopper added, "Was a

little dog . . . little black fellow. Didn't chase me, either."

Low as his voice had been, the man at the phone had heard him. He slammed down the receiver and came rushing. "What's that you said?" he cried. "What kind of a dog?"

Whopper backed away from him. What kind of trouble was coming now? Maybe he'd better go back to the police dog story. But the thought of Jess held him. He'd just have to stick to the truth.

"Sir," he muttered. "Just a wee little black dog it was. And its leash was tangled in the bushes so it couldn't chase me if it wanted to."

"What bushes?" the man asked excitedly. "Show me!"

More and more worried, Whopper led the way. The Scotty was still there, barking louder and louder as it tried to free itself.

"Dennis!" the man with Whopper yelled. "You little rascal!" He grabbed up the dog into his arms, freeing the leash with one hand.

"Little boy," he told Whopper, "you've done me a mighty good turn. Dennis here ran away today. We've been scouring the town for him. I was just phoning in a 'Lost and Found' ad, offering a reward. So I guess now you have that coming, haven't you?"

Whopper couldn't answer. His eyes were bulging out with excitement. He closed his hand over the bill the man slipped into it, and watched the stranger and his dog disappear down the block.

"Boy!" he said. He looked wide-eyed at the five-dollar bill he was holding. "Boy, now I have something to tell that doesn't *need* ex-ag-ger-ating!"

Stop and Think

1. What was Whopper's problem?

2. Who did Whopper promise that he would stop exaggerating?

3. What story did Whopper tell the man in the drugstore?

4. How was Whopper rewarded for telling the truth?

Storm at Sea

from *The Swiss Family Robinson*

For six days a fierce wind tore at our
sails. The white foam of the waves swept our
decks, and the tempest drove our ship so far
off course that no one on board knew where
we were. Everyone was worn out with toil
and care, and even the seamen fell on their
knees to pray to God for mercy.

My wife and four boys clung to me in
terror, but I told them, "God knows each rock
that lies hidden and sees each storm as it
comes. He can save us if it is His will. Yet if
He should think it good to call us to Him,

let us be thankful that we shall be together forever in Heaven." At these words, I saw my wife dry her tears, and from that time she was more calm.

All at once, above the roar of thundering waves, we heard the cry of "Land! Land!" In the same instant, the ship struck a rock with such force that we were all thrown off our feet. Then came a loud crack as if the ship had split in two. Leaving my family in our cabin in the boat's stern, I went up on deck. Just then I heard the captain call out, "Lower away the boats! We are lost!" My heart sank as I watched the sailors get into the last lifeboat, cut the rope, and leave us all alone. I cried out for them to wait, but my voice was lost in the roar of the waves.

The ship's stern, which held those most dear to me on earth, was jammed between two tall rocks. I could see in the south a line of rocky coast, which, though wild and bare, was now the aim of all my hopes, for there was no more aid to be had from man.

I left the deck to go below to my wife and boys. Putting on a calm look, I said, "Be of good cheer. If the wind dies down, we may yet reach the land."

This made my boys dry their tears, but my wife, who knew best how to read my thoughts, saw that I did not have much hope that the wind would die down. "Let us take some food," said she; "it will give us strength."

As night came on and it grew dark, we heard the wild waves boil with rage as they tore at the planks with a loud crash. "How could the sailors in the lifeboats survive in such a storm as this?" thought I.

The boys went to bed and slept, and my wife and I took our load of grief, doubts, and fears to the throne of God and left them there. Then my wife joined the boys below, and I stayed up on the deck to watch for morning.

Morning at Last

At long last, to my great joy, I saw the first faint streak of dawn. The wind was now calmer and the sea less rough, bringing a ray of hope to my heart. I went below to waken my wife and boys. Once they were on deck, the young ones were struck with awe to find no one there.

"The crew, where are they?" they cried. "Who is guiding the ship?"

"My boys," said I, "One stronger than man has brought us through it till now, and if He thinks fit, He will stretch out His arm to save us. Remember that God helps us when we help those around us. Now we must all search the ship for things we may need."

After some time, my family gathered around me again with the things they had found. Fifteen-year-old Fritz, the oldest boy, had found six guns and plenty of ammunition. Ernest, who was twelve, brought an axe, a spade, knives, nails, and the like. Franz, the youngest, who was nearly eight, brought a box full of fish hooks.

"For my part," said my wife, "I bring good news. Franz and I have found a cow, a donkey, two goats, six sheep, a ram, and a fine sow. We have fed them, and I hope they will do well."

"And I have found two big dogs," said ten-year-old Jack. "They can help us hunt when we get to land."

"Ah!" said I, "but can you tell us how to reach land?"

"Yes," replied Jack, "We can each get into a big tub and float to shore. I went across Aunt's pond that way once."

"A good thought!" said I. "Be quick, boys; give me the saw and some nails, and we will see what we can do."

A Raft of Tubs

I found some empty barrels in the ship's hold, and we rolled four of them up on deck. They were made of strong wood and were bound with metal hoops. In fact, they were just the right thing. My boys and I cut each of the four barrels in two with our saw, and then we fastened all eight tubs together.

At last we saw with joy our small fleet of boats all in a line. "I could not trust my life to one of those tubs!" cried my wife. But I told her to wait till the work was done. I then found a long, thin plank and put the tubs on it. We nailed the tubs to the plank, nailed more boards to each side, and soon had ourselves a strange little boat.

Once we had gotten it into the water, the boys all stood on the ship's deck in great joy to see the boat glide off and then float like a swan on the waves. Had it not been for the rope, it would have gone off to sea. We next found some oars and, our work done for the day, sat down to a meal, for we had hardly had time to snatch a piece of bread all day. When we finally went to rest, we were much more at ease than we had been the night before.

At dawn we all woke up, and after prayers, I said, "We must now, my dear boys, embark on the wide sea in search of a home. Give all the animals enough food to last them for several days. By then we may be able to come back and rescue them, too. Are you all here? Get what you wish to take with you, but let it be things that will meet our needs when we get to land."

I had put the guns on our raft, and I told

my wife and the lads to bring some big bags, a chest of tools and nails, and sails for making a tent.

Just before we got on board, we heard the rooster give a loud crow as if to remind us that we had left no food for him and the twelve hens. So I put them all into one of the extra tubs on our boat and put a lid over them. I let the other birds loose. The geese and ducks started to swim to shore at once, and the pigeons flew there with great joy.

At last, after praying for God's blessing, we each took our place on the raft. In the first tub sat my wife, in the next, Franz, in the third, Fritz, in the fourth, Jack. The fifth tub held the rooster and the hens, and the sixth held all sorts of food and other stores. Ernest was in the seventh tub, and I in the eighth. My task was to guide the boat that held all that was most dear to me in this world.

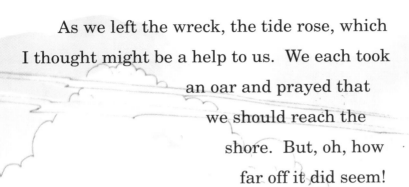

As we left the wreck, the tide rose, which
I thought might be a help to us. We each took
an oar and prayed that
we should reach the
shore. But, oh, how
far off it did seem!

For some
time the boat just
turned around and around.
But at last I figured out how to
steer it so as to make it go straight.

As soon as the two dogs saw us leave the

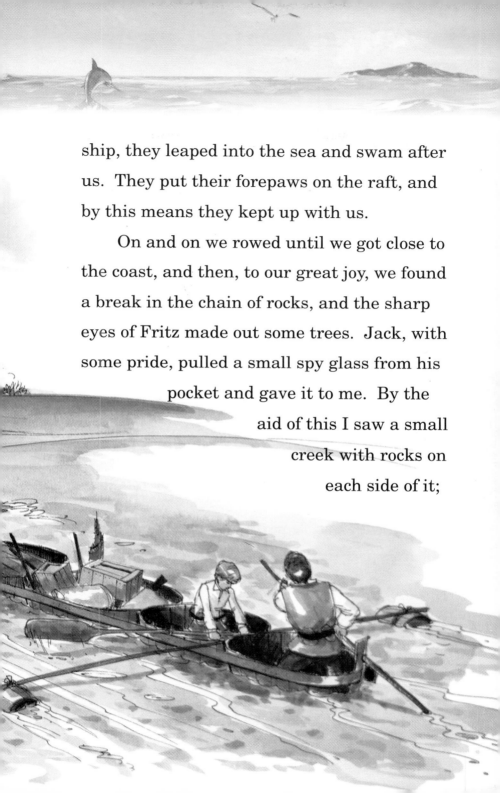

ship, they leaped into the sea and swam after us. They put their forepaws on the raft, and by this means they kept up with us.

On and on we rowed until we got close to the coast, and then, to our great joy, we found a break in the chain of rocks, and the sharp eyes of Fritz made out some trees. Jack, with some pride, pulled a small spy glass from his pocket and gave it to me. By the aid of this I saw a small creek with rocks on each side of it;

and as I found that the ducks and geese were swimming toward it, I knew it was all right. It was a small bay with a beach that made a good place to land.

The Deserted Island

Joyfully, we all jumped out of our tubs and looked around us. The dogs, which were the first to get to shore, leaped around us, barking wildly. The ducks and geese kept up their cry; and the hens, when we let them loose, lent their cluck. The rooster crowed triumphantly. All these sounds, with the noise of the boys' talk, made a strange din.

The first thing we did when we came safely to land was to bow down and give thanks to God, in Whose hands were our lives. "If we make God our guide," I told them all, "how can we go wrong? If we make Him our shield, why need we fear? If we make His Word the lamp

of our feet, how can we stray? He is our life, our God, our all; the Lord is our strength."

We took all of our possessions out of the boat, and how rich we felt with these few things! After finding a good place for our tent in the shade of the rocks, we set to work with a pole and pegs, and then we brought out the food.

I sent my sons to fetch some grass and moss to spread in the sun to dry. "That will make good mattresses for us to sleep on at night," I explained. While all the boys were at work at this, I found a flat place near a stream to serve as our kitchen.

It did not take long to light up a bright fire of dry twigs; then I put into the pot some squares of dried soup that we had found in the ship and left my wife and Franz to cook the meal. Fritz took one of the guns with him to the side of the stream, and Ernest headed for the coast. Jack set off for a ridge of rocks that ran down to the sea to look for shellfish.

Before long, alarmed at hearing Jack's screams, I grabbed my axe and ran to his aid. I found him up to his knees in a pool with a huge lobster, his leg caught in its powerful claw. Though the lobster slid away when I

came up, I did not lose sight of it, and as Jack
had a mind to take it home, I caught it
for him.

When we got back to the tent,
Jack cried in a loud voice, "A
lobster! Such a huge lobster!
Ernest! Where's Fritz? Be
careful it doesn't bite you,
Franz!"

Ernest
thought the
lobster would
be a good thing
to add to the
soup, but my wife
set it aside for the
next day. I then
went back to the
place where we had caught it and brought to

shore several barrels that I had seen floating in the sea from the wreck.

I told Jack that he was the first boy to bring us food, for none of the rest had done so.

"I saw some oysters on a rock," said Ernest, "but I couldn't get at them, because the sea made my feet wet."

"Ernest," said I, "I must beg of you to get us some. We must all work for the good of the rest and not worry about wet feet, for the sun soon dries them."

My wife used a small stick to stir the pot. When she tasted some of the soup that clung to it, she said, "The soup is good, but how are we to drink it? We don't have any plates or spoons, and we certainly can't raise this large pot to our lips."

We all cast grave looks at the pot, and all at once we burst out in laughter at our sad plight.

"If we had some coconuts," said Ernest, "we could split them and make both spoons and plates with them!"

"If," said I; "but we have none! If wishing did any good, we might as well wish for some fine gold spoons."

"Well," said Ernest, "we can use oyster shells."

"That is a good thought," said I. "Run off, Ernest, at once, and get some."

At these words, off ran Jack, who was up to his knees in the sea by the time that Ernest had reached the spot. He tore down the shells from the rocks and threw them to Ernest, who put them into his bag. Then the two boys came racing back with their finds.

Fritz had not yet come home, and my wife was worried that something had happened to him, but just then we heard his voice call to us from some way off. He told us he had been on the left side of the stream, where the land lies low, and had found many barrels, chests, planks, and all sorts of other things from the wreck.

"In the morning we will go and get them," I said. "Then we can go back to the ship to check on the animals. We must have the cow, at least: our bread would not be half as hard if we had some milk to soak it in."

"I also found a grove of trees," said Fritz, "and some rich grass for the cow."

"Good," said I. "We'll make good use of that tomorrow. But first tell me, did you see a trace of our poor shipmates?"

"No sign at all of man on land or sea," answered Fritz. "We seem to be all alone here."

The time had now come to sit down to our meal of soup. The boys all burnt their hands at first, but soon we were experts at using our oyster-shell spoons.

After we ate, the hens and other fowls came around us to pick up the crumbs.

My wife then took out her bag and fed them some grain. When they had had their fill, the pigeons flew to the rocks, the hens and rooster perched on top of the tent, and the ducks and geese went to roost in a marsh near the sea.

The sun sank all at once, and it was time for us to rest. We took care to load the guns, then knelt down to pray and went to our beds of moss. Before long, we were all fast asleep.

This story is just the beginning of the wonderful book, *Swiss Family Robinson*. When you are a little older, you will enjoy reading the rest of their adventures.

Stop and Think

1. Tell how many people were in the Robinson family.

2. How did the Robinson family end up alone on an island?

3. How did they get to shore?

4. Who did they thank for getting them safely through the storm?

5. What did they use to eat their soup?

6. Where did the animals and supplies come from that the family was able to use?

	leggings	moccasins
	homespun	tassel
	chinks	saucy
coarse	trudged	wistfully

fodder corn: corn fed to farm animals

A Lad of Long Ago

Abe hurried home as fast as his feet
would carry him. Perhaps if he had worn soft
wool stockings and finely fitting shoes, like
yours, he could have run faster. But, instead
of stockings, he wore deerskin leggings, and
pulled over these were clumsy moccasins of
bearskin that his mother had made for him.

Such a funny little figure he was, trudg-
ing along across the rough fields! His suit
was of warm, gray homespun. His odd-shaped
cap had once been on the back of a coon.

The coon's tail flew out behind as he walked—like a funny, furry tassel. But if you could have looked into the honest, twinkling, blue eyes of this little lad of long ago you would have liked him at once.

In one hand Abe held something very precious. It wasn't a purse of gold, nor a bag of gold. It was only a book, but Abe thought more of that book than he would of gold or precious stones. To know just what that book meant to Abe, you must be very fond of reading. You must think how it would seem to live far away from all the schools, to have no books of your own, and to see no books anywhere, except two or three old ones of your mother's that you had read over and over until you knew them by heart.

So, when a neighbor had said that Abe might take a book home and keep it until he had read it all through, do you wonder that his eyes shone like stars? A real book—a book that told about boys and girls and the big world! Abe's heart beat fast; it seemed almost too good to be true.

Abe's home was built on a hillside. It was not much like your home. It was not built of stone or brick, not even of nice, smooth lumber, but of rough logs. When Abe lay in his small bed, close to the roof, he could look through the chinks between the logs and see the great, white stars shining down on him.

Sometimes the great yellow moon smiled at him as she sailed through the dark night sky. And sometimes, too, saucy raindrops pattered down on the little face on the coarse pillow.

Tonight, after Abe had crept up the steps to the loft, he put his precious book in a small crack between the logs. When the first gray light came in, in the morning, he awoke and read until his father called him to get up. Night after night he read, until the book was nearly finished. Abe worked hard all day long, and never a minute had he in the daytime to peep between the covers of his beloved book.

One night he slipped the book away as usual and fell asleep to dream of the wonderful story. He awoke very early, but there were no golden sunbeams to peep through the chinks and play across his pillow. The loft was dark and Abe could hear the wind whistling out in the trees. He reached out his hand for the book—and what do you think?—He put it into a pile of something white and cold lying on his bed! His little bed was covered with an outside blanket of soft, white snow!

He shivered and sat up, reaching again for the book. He pulled it out. Then the poor little fellow almost cried—for that precious book was wet from cover to cover, and its crisp leaves were crumpled and soaked from the heavy fall of snow.

Poor Abe! He sat up in his cold bed and brushed off the snow as best he could. He could scarcely keep the tears back. There was a big lump in his throat, and a big lump in his heart. What would the kind neighbor say?

As soon as he could, Abe set off across the snowy fields to the kind neighbor's house. It was more than a mile away, but he trudged along, not thinking of the wind or the cold, but only of the book. When he found the neighbor he held out the poor, spoiled book, and, looking straight up into the man's face, with clear, honest eyes, he told his sad little story.

"Well, my boy," said the man, smiling down into the sober little face, "so my book is spoiled. Will you work for me to pay for it?"

"I will do anything for you," said the little fellow, eagerly.

"Well, then, I will ask you to pull fodder corn for me for three days," said the man.

Abe looked up into his kind face.

"Then, sir," he said, wistfully, "will the book be all mine?"

"Why, yes, of course," said the man, good-naturedly, "you may have the book; you will earn it."

So Abe went to work for three days. He was cold, and his back ached as he pulled corn for the cattle, but he was too happy to mind, for was not that precious book to be soon his very own?

What do you suppose the book was, for which Abe worked so long and faithfully? Was it a book of wonderful fairy tales? No; the book was the story of George Washington. And, long years afterward, when Abe had grown to be a great man and the President of

the United States, he used to tell the story of
his first book.

"That book—the story of George Washington—helped me to become the President,"
he said.

1. What treasure did Abe's neighbor loan him?

2. Why was a book a treasure to Abe?

3. What happened to the borrowed book?

4. What did Abe do that shows he was honest?

5. How did Abe pay for the book?

6. Who was the book about?

LINCOLN

There was a boy of other days,
A quiet, awkward, earnest lad,
Who trudged long weary miles to get
A book on which his heart was set—
And then no candle had!

He was too poor to buy a lamp
But very wise in woodmen's ways.
He gathered seasoned bough and stem,
And crisping leaf, and kindled them
Into a ruddy blaze.

Then as he lay full length and read,
The firelight flickered on his face,
And etched his shadow on the gloom.
And made a picture in the room,
In that most humble place.

The hard years came, the hard years went,
But, gentle, brave, and strong of will,
He met them all. And when to-day
We see his pictured face, we say,
"There's light upon it still."

—*Nancy Byrd Turner*

Word Watch

Hector Marcano (hĕc′tər mär·kä′nō)

Sanchez (sän′chĕz)

Venezuela (vĕn·ĭ·zwā′lə)

immediately errand hurriedly hesitating

tortilla (tôr·tē′ə): a thin, flat, round cake made
of cornmeal or flour
shuffle: to drag the feet while walking

Hector and His Conscience

"I need a job," Hector began, as he walked into the small store. "The only way I will be able to go to camp is to work and earn some money. Mr. Sanchez, could you use me to work for you in your shoe store?"

"As a matter of fact, Hector, I do need a boy to begin immediately. Could you do that?"

"Oh, yes, sir! I could, sir! And I will work hard for you," replied the boy.

Hector Marcano lived in a city in Venezuela where shoes were made and sold. It was true he needed money to go to camp, but he also needed shoes to wear right now. His parents were poor, and with 10 children younger than he in the home, there was no money for Hector's shoes.

One day while Mr. Sanchez went on an errand, a delivery boy brought an order of shoes to the store. Hector noticed the order said, "12 pairs." Silently he checked to see if there were that many. "One, two, three, four, five, six, seven, eight, nine, ten, eleven, twelve . . . thirteen!" Hurriedly he signed the slip to show that he had received them, and off went the delivery boy.

As Hector looked through the boxes, he noticed a pair just his size. Without hesitating, he slipped the box under his arm and ran through the streets to his home. Silently he put the box behind the trunk—the only piece of furniture in the room. Wasn't he fortunate, he thought. No one was at home, no one to ask him any questions, no one to know about the shoes. All the way home he kept thinking of something the missionary had said: "The eyes of the Lord are in every place."

As he returned to the store, he breathed a sigh of relief, "Good! I have returned before Mr. Sanchez. He won't know that I have the shoes."

"Hector, has a shipment of shoes been delivered?" asked Mr. Sanchez as he walked in the store.

"Yes, sir! Here it is," Hector proudly announced. "I counted them—12 pairs, and 12 pairs ordered," he pointed to the order.

"But I just came from Mr. Lopez's, where the shoes are made. I asked him to send 13 pairs instead of 12 this time. I saw him give another box to the delivery boy. That boy can't be trusted! I will tell Mr. Lopez. He will have him fired. He doesn't deserve to have a job!" Mr. Sanchez was getting more angry by the minute.

That evening Hector slowly shuffled his bare feet along the dirty path. There was not much joy in going home tonight.

"Hello, Hector," greeted his mother cheerily, "I have some good tortillas and soup for dinner."

"I don't want any, Mama," replied Hector, and off he went to sit alone in a corner of the patio.

Mama noticed that her oldest boy was acting strangely, so she put her hand on his forehead and asked if he had a fever. No, he seemed cool. Hector was awake long after all the other children were sleeping that night.

"Tell me, my boy," asked Mrs. Marcano, "what is wrong?"

"The missionary said, 'The eyes of the Lord are in every place,' didn't he, Mama?"

"Yes," replied the mother.

"And he also said, 'Be sure your sins will find you out.' "

"Yes, Son, he did—for that's what the Bible says."

"But, Mama, I am a thief, and that isn't all. I am causing a boy to lose his job."

"Sin always hurts someone, my boy," replied the mother. "But, Hector, remember the missionary also said that the Lord Jesus Christ died for our sins. If we let Him, He will take them away and make us clean again."

Hector began to cry, as he said to God, "I don't deserve that You should love me, God, but since You do and since Your Son Jesus died for my sins, I want Him to live in my heart and chase all these bad things out. Come into my heart, Lord Jesus." How glad he was that Somebody loved him, Somebody who could really forgive him and change his heart!

"Now, Son, you have sinned against God, but He has forgiven you because you believed Jesus died for your sin. But you have also sinned against Mr. Sanchez. Tomorrow you must ask Mr. Sanchez to forgive you, and you must return the shoes. The Lord Jesus will give you the courage."

The hours before morning seemed to drag for Hector. Finally it was time to go to work. He felt like turning back many times as he shuffled along the dirt road. Each time he talked to the Lord Jesus, "Dear Jesus, I don't have the courage, but You promised You would help me."

Mr. Sanchez was already in the store. Before Hector realized it, he had begun: "Mr. Sanchez, I stole the pair of shoes yesterday,

and I am sorry. I return them to you now and ask your forgiveness. I sinned against God and you. I have asked God to forgive me, and He has, because His Son Jesus died for my sins. He took them all away when I told Him I am a sinner and thanked Him for dying for me."

"Where are you going, Hector," called Mr. Sanchez, as Hector began walking out of the store.

"You won't want me to work for you any more," Hector said sadly. "I don't deserve to be trusted."

"Oh, but, Hector, I *know* I can trust you now. I have noticed others who have accepted Jesus as Savior. Everybody knows they become honest people. And, Hector, I am going to raise your salary," Mr. Sanchez finished.

"Oh, Mr. Sanchez, I thank you! I do want to work for you. I will ask Jesus every day to help me do a good job. But I want to go to camp in just three weeks. Could you spare me to be away for two weeks?"

"Of course, my boy."

So Hector walked home with a spring in his step, for his conscience was clear toward God and toward men.

Stop and Think

1. Why did Hector want to find a job?

2. Tell how Hector got the new pair of shoes. Was it honest?

3. Who did Mr. Sanchez think had been dishonest?

Cornelius and His
Bean Tree

There was once a man in Ceylon named
Cornelius who loved to sit on his veranda and
dream. One day, seeing that a fine bean tree
in his garden was full of blossoms, he said to
himself, "In a little while I shall have a lot of
beans on that tree. I will take them to the
market and sell them for a good price. Then
I will buy some coconuts, and selling them also,
I will buy some fowls. The ships in the harbor
will give me much money for them, and then I
shall have enough money to set up a new business. I shall go into partnership with an Indian

167

merchant and marry my daughter to his eldest son. And *then* I shall be able to build a fine row of shops on this piece of ground, and I shall be a rich man."

Cornelius stopped planning and looked at the bean tree with a happy smile; the next instant he frowned. "This will never do," he said. "The bean tree stands just on the spot where I want my shops."

Cornelius sprang up, seized an axe, and cut the tree to the ground. At that moment his wife came onto the veranda. "What is my husband doing?" she said. "Why is the tree laid low?"

"Do not be disturbed in mind," said Cornelius.

"Soon you will be a rich lady with silk to wear and fine jewels," and he told her all he had planned.

"But you have cut down the tree that was to begin our fortune!" his wife cried, and then, only then, the folly of his deed dawned on her husband's mind.

So in Ceylon today, when a foolish thing is said or done, people say, "That is like cutting down the bean tree!"

Stop and Think

1. What did Cornelius love to do?

2. How did he plan to become a rich man?

3. Why did Cornelius cut down the bean tree?

4. Who made Cornelius see that he had done a foolish thing?

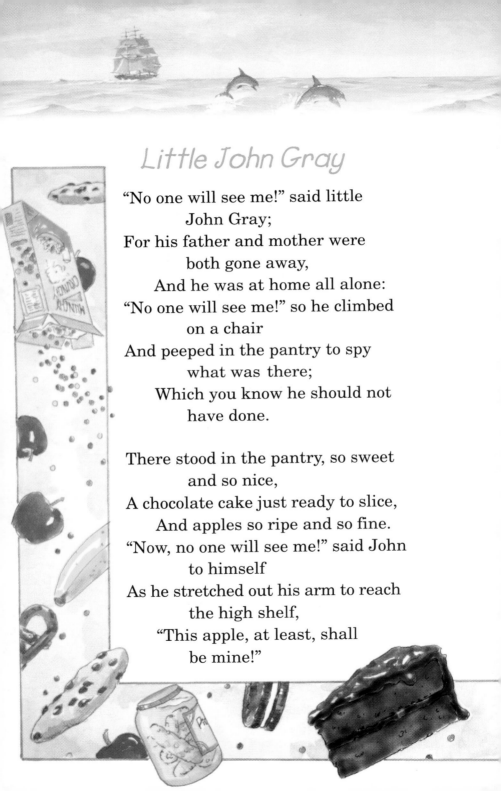

Little John Gray

"No one will see me!" said little
    John Gray;
For his father and mother were
    both gone away,
    And he was at home all alone:
"No one will see me!" so he climbed
    on a chair
And peeped in the pantry to spy
    what was there;
    Which you know he should not
    have done.

There stood in the pantry, so sweet
    and so nice,
A chocolate cake just ready to slice,
    And apples so ripe and so fine.
"Now, no one will see me!" said John
    to himself
As he stretched out his arm to reach
    the high shelf,
    "This apple, at least, shall
    be mine!"

John paused, and put back the nice
    apple so red;
For he thought of the words his
    kind mother had said
      When she left all these things
      in his care.
"But no one will see me!" thought
    he, "is not true;
For I've read that God sees us in all
    that we do,
      And is with us wherever we are."

Well done! Your kind father and
    mother obey;
Try ever to please them, and mind
    what they say,
      Even when they are absent
      from you;
And never forget, that though no
    one be nigh,
You cannot be hid from the gaze of
    God's eye—
      For He notices all that you do.

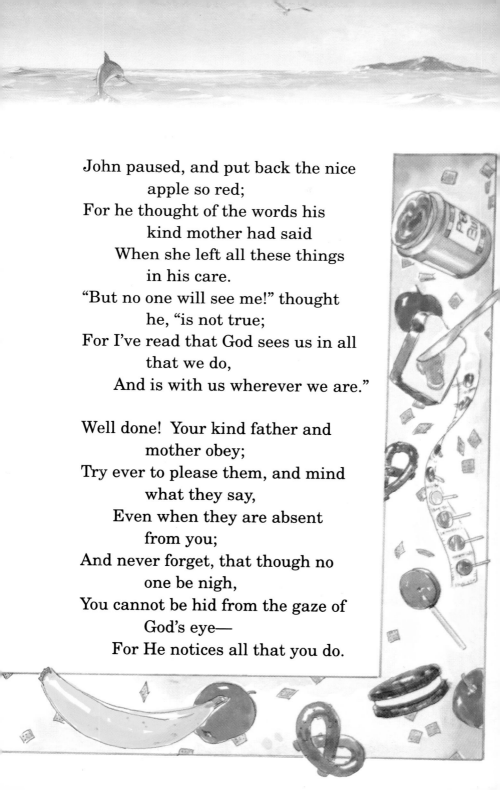

Lucien (loo′·shen)

unconcerned   reverently
anxious   smothered
unshuttered   downy

fork (of the road): a road that divides and
goes off in two directions

Christmas with the Angels

from *Treasures Of The Snow*

It was Christmas Eve, and three people
were climbing the steep white mountainside.
The moonlight was casting shadows behind
them across the snow. The middle one was a
woman with a dark cloak over her shoulders.
Clinging to her hand was a black-haired boy,
aged six, who talked all the time with his
mouth full. Walking near, with her eyes
turned to the stars, was a little girl of seven.
Her hands were folded across her chest. Close

against her heart she carried a golden gingerbread bear with eyes made of white icing.

The little boy had also had a gingerbread bear, but he had eaten it all except the back legs. He looked at the little girl with a grudge in his eye. "Mine was bigger than yours," he said.

The little girl seemed unconcerned. "I would not change," she replied. Then she looked down again with eyes full of love at the beautiful gingerbread creature in her arms. How solid he looked, how good he smelled, and how bright he appeared in the starlight.

She would never eat him, never! Eighty little village children had been given gingerbread bears, but to her it seemed she had the most beautiful.

Yes, she would keep him forever in memory of tonight. Whenever she looked at him she would remember Christmas Eve— the frosty blue sky, the warm glow of the lighted church, the tree dressed with the silver stars, the carols, the crib, and the sweet, sad story of Christmas. It made her want to cry when she thought about the inn where there was no room for Jesus. She would have opened her house door wide and welcomed them in.

Lucien, the boy, wanted her to talk. "I have nearly finished mine," he remarked. "Let me taste yours, Annette; you have not begun it." But Annette shook her head and

held her bear a little closer. "I am never
going to eat him," she replied; "I am going to
keep him forever and ever."

They had come to a parting of the ways.
The crumbly white snow-path lined with the
sled tracks divided. A few hundred yards
along the right fork stood a group of houses
with lights shining in their windows and
dark barns behind them. Annette was nearly
home.

Madame Morel stopped. "Are you all
right to run home alone, Annette?" she asked.
"Or shall we take you to the door?"

"Oh, I would much rather go alone,"
answered Annette, "and thank you for taking
me. Good night, Madame; good night,
Lucien."

She turned and ran for fear Madame
would change her mind and insist on seeing

her to the door, when she wanted to be alone
with her thoughts.

She wanted
to get away from
Lucien's chatter
and wrap herself
up with the si-
lence of the night.
How could she
think, and look at
the stars, when
she was having to make polite replies to
Madame Morel and Lucien?

She had never been out alone at night
before. She was to have gone to the church
on the sleigh with her father and mother;
they had all been thinking about it and planning it for weeks. But that morning her
mother had become ill, and her father had
gone off on the midday train to fetch the

doctor from the town up the valley. The doctor had arrived about teatime, but he could not cure her in time to go to church as Annette had hoped he would. So to her great disappointment she had had to go with Madam Morel from the house up the hill. But when she had reached the church, it had been so beautiful that she had forgotten everything but the tree and Christmas, so it had not mattered so much.

Now, as she stood alone among snow and stars, it seemed a pity to go in just yet. Just opposite stood the cowshed; Annette could hear the beasts moving and munching their food. A glorious idea struck her. She made up her mind in a moment, darted across the sleigh tracks and lifted the latch of the door. The smell of cattle and milk and hay came to her as she slipped inside; she wriggled between the legs of the cow and wormed her

way into the hayrack. The cow was having supper, but Annette flung her arms around her neck and let her go on munching. Surely the cows munched that way when Mary sat among them with her newborn Baby Jesus in her arms, Annette thought.

She looked down at the manger, and to her it seemed as though the heavenly Jesus were lying in the straw, with the cows worshiping about Him. Through a hole in the roof she could see one bright star, and she remembered how a star had shined over Bethlehem and guided the wise men to the house where Jesus lay. She could imagine them walking up the valley on their swaying camels. Perhaps any moment now the door would open softly, and the shepherds would come in with little lambs in their arms and offer to cover the Child with woolly sheep fleeces. As Annette leaned over, a great pity swept over her for the homeless Baby Jesus, because all doors had been shut against Him.

"There would have been plenty of room in our home," she whispered. "Perhaps, after

all, this is the nicest place. The hay is sweet and clean, and Louise's breath is warm and pleasant. Maybe God chose the best cradle for His Baby after all."

She might have stayed there dreaming all night had it not been for the gleam of a lantern through the half-open door of the shed and the sound of footsteps in the snow. Then she heard her father call her in an anxious voice.

She slipped down from the rack, dodged Louise's tail, and ran out to him with wide open arms.

"I went in to wish the cows a happy Christmas," she said, laughing. "Did you come out to find me?"

"Yes, I did," he replied, but he was not laughing. His face was pale and grave in the moonlight. He took her hand and almost dragged her up the steps. "You should have come in at once when your mother is so ill. She has been asking for you this last half-hour."

Annette's heart smote her dreadfully, for somehow the Christmas tree had driven everything else out of her mind. All the time, her mother whom she loved so much was lying ill and wanting her. She had thought the doctor would have made her well. She drew her hand from her father's and ran up the wooden stairs and slipped into her mother's bedroom.

Neither the doctor nor the village nurse saw her until she had crept up to the bed, for she was a small, slim child who moved as noiselessly as a shadow. But her mother saw her, and half held out her arms. Annette ran into them and hid her face on her mother's shoulder. She began to cry quietly, for her mother's face was almost as white as the pillow, and it frightened

her. Besides, she felt sorry for having been away so long.

"Annette," whispered her mother, "stop crying; I have a present for you."

Annette stopped at once. A present? Of course, it was Christmas. She had forgotten. Her mother always gave her a present. Wherever could it be? She looked around.

Her mother turned to the nurse. "Give it to her," she whispered. And the nurse drew back the blanket and produced a bundle wrapped in a white shawl. She came to Annette and held it out to her.

"Your little brother," she explained. "Let us go down by the fire, and you shall rock his cradle. We must leave your mother to sleep. Kiss her good night."

"Your little brother," echoed her mother's weak voice. "He is yours, Annette. Bring him up and love him and look after him for me. I give him to you."

Her voice trailed away, and she closed her eyes. Annette, too dazed to speak, allowed herself to be led downstairs by the nurse. She sat down on a stool by the stove to rock the wooden cradle where her Christmas present lay smothered in shawls and blankets.

She sat very still for a long time staring
at the hump that was her little brother. The
snow cast a strange light on the walls, and
the glow of the stove burned. The house was
very, very still, and the Christmas star shone
in through the unshuttered windows. So had
it shone on that other Christ-
mas Baby in the stable at
Bethlehem,

and so had Mary sat and watched God's little Son, just as she was sitting by the stove watching little brother.

She put out shy fingers and touched the top of his head, which was all she could see of him. Then with a tired sigh she leaned her head against the cradle—stars, shepherds, little new babies, shut doors, wise men and gingerbread bears—they all became muddled up in her mind, and she slid on to the floor.

And it was here that her father found her an hour later, lying asleep as her baby brother, her bright head pillowed on the cradle rocker.

"Poor little motherless creatures," he said as he stooped to pick her up; "how shall I ever bring them up without their mother?"

For Annette's mother had gone to spend Christmas with the angels.

Treasures of the Snow is a favorite book of Christian fiction. It is full of adventure. Read the entire book to find out what lies ahead for Lucien, Annette, and Annette's baby brother.

Stop and Think

1. What special day was it when this story took place?

2. What had the children been given at the church service?

3. Why had Annette gone to the service with Madame Morel and Lucien rather than her parents?

4. What Christmas gift did Annette's mother give her that night?

Word Watch

anxiety   nuisance

skeleton   intelligent

hesitated   wheelbarrow

Cockletop   Bobtail

hobble: to limp; to walk awkwardly

burr: a prickly seed

Nobody's Horse

"Oh, Mother, don't let them kill him! He isn't doing any harm, and he is so old and weak. Besides, he hasn't anyone to be good to him except Posy and me!" cried Ned, bursting into his mother's room, breathless with anxiety and haste.

"Kill whom, dear? Sit down and tell me all about it," said his mother.

"I can't sit down, and I must be quick, for they may do it while I'm gone. I left Posy to watch him, and she is going to scream with

187

all her might the minute she sees them coming back!" cried Ned.

"Mercy on us! What is it, child?" said his
mother.

" A dear old horse, Mother, who has been
hobbling around the roads for a week. The
neighbors all drive him away; so Posy and I
give him clover and pat him. Today we found
him at our gate, looking over at us playing in
the field. I was going to let him in, but Mr.
White came along and drove him off. He said
he is to be killed because he has no master
and is a nuisance to the neighborhood. Oh,
Mother, don't let him do it, please!"

"But Neddy, I cannot take him in, as I
did the lame chicken and the cat without a
tail. He is too big and eats too much, and we
have no barn. Mr. White can find his master,
perhaps, or use him for light work."

But his mother could go no further, for Ned said again, "No, he can't, Mother. He says the poor old thing is of no use at all. And his master won't be found, because he has gone away and left old Major to take care of himself. Mr. White knew the man and says he had Major for eighteen years, and he was a good horse, and now he is left all alone."

"It was cruel, Neddy, and we must see what we can do about it."

So his mother put down her work and followed her boy, who raced before to tell Posy it would be all right now.

Mrs. West found her small daughter perched on a stone wall, patting the head of a very old horse that looked like a skeleton rather than a living animal. Ned gave a whoop as he came, and the poor beast hastily hobbled across the road, pressing himself into

a clump of blackberry bushes, as if trying to get out of sight.

"That's the way he does when anyone comes, because the boys tease him, and people drive him about until he doesn't know what to do. Isn't it a pity to see him so afraid, Mother?" said tenderhearted Ned, as he pulled a big handful of clover for him.

Indeed, it was sad, for the poor thing had been a fine horse once. One could see that by his intelligent eyes and the gentle way in which he looked about him as if asking a little kindness in return for his long faithfulness.

"See his poor legs all swelled up, and the

bones in his back, and the burrs the bad boys put in his mane, and the dusty grass he has to eat. Look! he knows me and isn't afraid, because I'm good to him," said Ned, patting old Major, who gratefully ate fresh clover from the friendly little hand.

"Yes, and he lets me stroke his nose, Mother. It's as soft as velvet, and his big eyes don't frighten me a bit, because they are so gentle. Oh, if we could only put him in our field and keep him till he dies, I should be so happy," said Posy, with such a coaxing arm around her mother's neck that it was very hard to deny her anything.

Ned's Strange Request
"If you will let me have Major, I won't ask for any other birthday present," cried Ned, as the old horse rubbed his gray head against the boy's shoulder.

"Why, Neddy! Do you really mean that?
I was going to give you something you want
very much. Shall I give you an old worn-out
horse instead?" asked his mother, surprised
but pleased at the offer.

Ned looked at her, then at old Major, and
hesitated; for he guessed that the other gift
was the wheelbarrow he had wanted so long.
He had seen it at the store and tried it, and it
had such a delightful creak and rumble to it.
He had planned to push everything in it from
Posy to a load of hay. Yes, it must be his, and
Major must be left to look out for himself.

Just as he decided this, however, Posy
gave a cry that told him Mr. White was coming. Major pressed farther into the prickly
bushes, with a patient sort of sigh and a look
that seemed to say: "Good-bye, little friend.
Don't give up anything for me. I'm not worth
it, for I can only love you in return."

Mr. White was very near, but Major was safe; for with a sudden redness in his freckled face, Ned put his arm on the poor beast's neck and said bravely, "I choose him, Mother. Now he's mine, and I would like to see anybody touch him."

It was a pretty sight—the generous little lad defending the old horse and loving him.

Posy clapped her hands, and Mother smiled with a bright look at her boy, while Mr. White threw over his arm the halter with which he was about to lead the old horse away.

"I don't want to hurt the poor old beast, ma'am, but he's no use at all, and folks complain of his being in the way. So I thought the kindest thing was to put him out of his misery," said Mr. White.

"Does he suffer, do you think?" said Mrs. West. "If he does, of course, it would be no kindness to keep him alive."

"Well, no, I don't suppose he suffers except for food and a little care. But if he can't have them, it will go hard with him," answered Mr. White.

"He never should have been left in this forlorn way. Those who had him in his youth and strength should have cared for him in his old age," said Mrs. West.

"So they should, ma'am, but Miller was a mean man, and when he moved, he just left the old horse to live or die, though he told me himself that Major had served him well for nearly twenty years. What do you intend to do about it, ma'am?" said Mr. White.

"I'll show you, sir," said Mrs. West.

"Ned, open the gate and lead old Major in. This field shall be his home while he lives, for so faithful a servant has earned his rest, and shall have it."

"All right, ma'am, I haven't a word to say against it," said Mr. White, pleasantly, as he walked away. But somehow his barn did not look as handsome to him as usual when he thought that his neighbor, who had no barn, had taken the friendless horse in.

Old Major's Happy Home

It was difficult to make Major enter the field, for he had been turned out of so many fields and had been driven away from so many lawns, that he could not understand the invitation to enter a great green field with apple trees for shade and a brook running through the middle of it.

When, at last, he stepped into the field,

it was both sad and funny to see how hard he tried to show his delight.

First, he sniffed the air. Then he nibbled the sweet grass, and, taking a long look about him, he surprised the children by lying down and trying to roll over. He could not do it, however, and so he lay still with his head stretched out, gently flapping his tail, as if to say—"It's all right, my dears. I'm not very strong, and joy upsets me; but I'm quite comfortable, bless you!"

"Isn't it fine to see him safe and happy, Mother?" said Posy while Ned sat down beside his horse and began to take the burrs out of his mane.

"Very fine; only don't kill him with kindness, and be careful not to get hurt," answered her mother as she went back to her sewing, feeling as if she had bought an elephant and didn't know what to do with it.

Later in the day a sudden shower came up, and Mrs. West looked about to see if the children were under cover, for they played out in the open all day long if possible.

"Have you seen the children, Sally?" she said to the cook, after calling them and getting no answer.

"Ned's down in the pasture, mum, holding an umbrella over that old horse, and he's got a raincoat on him, too. Calvin saw it, and he almost died laughing," said Sally, shaking her fat sides with laughter.

Mother laughed, too, but asked if Ned had on his boots and coat.

"Yes, mum, but I never imagined what the dear was up to till Calvin told me. Posy wanted to go, but I wouldn't let her, and so she went up to the upper window, where she can see under the umbrella."

Mrs. West went up to find her little girl gazing over at the field with a happy, satisfied look on her face. For there, under the

apple tree, stood Major, covered with the old raincoat, while his new master held an umbrella over his aged head with a patience that made him very dear to his mother's heart.

Fortunately, the shower was soon over, and Ned came in to dry himself, not knowing that he had done anything funny. Then his mother suggested that they could build a shed for Major out of some rough boards on the place. Ned was full of interest at once, and with some help from Calvin, built a shelter in a corner under the old apple tree. There was no need for an umbrella after that.

So Major lived in clover and was a happy horse. Cockletop, the lame chicken, and Bobtail, the cat, welcomed him and became his fast friends. Cockletop chased grasshoppers or pecked about his feet while he was fed, and Bobtail rubbed against his legs and slept in his shed.

But Major loved the children best. It was pleasant to see him watch for them, with ears cocked at the first sound of their voices,

his dim eyes brightening at the sight of their happy faces peeping over the wall.

Stop and Think

1. Why were Ned and Posy so upset?

2. What was the horse's name?

3. What was wrong with Major?

4. What was Ned willing to do if his mother let him keep the horse?

The Bible Says,

"A righteous man regardeth the life of his beast: but the tender mercies of the wicked are cruel."

Proverbs 12:10

The Pasture

I'm going out to clean
    the pasture spring;
I'll only stop to rake the
    leaves away
(And wait to watch the
    water clear, I may):
I shan't be gone long.—
    You come too.

I'm going out to fetch
    the little calf
That's standing by the mother.
    It's so young
It totters when she licks it
    with her tongue.
I shan't be gone long.—
    You come too.

—*Robert Frost*

The Prisoner and the Shipwreck

from Acts 27

"All aboard!" cried the captain of a sailing vessel which was just loosing from the wharf to sail out to sea. There, on the deck, were a number of prisoners, guarded by soldiers. One of these prisoners was Paul, who had been seized in the temple at Jerusalem and nearly killed by a riotous mob for preaching the gospel.

Forty men had secretly vowed not to eat or drink until they had killed him. Paul's nephew had found out about the plot, and Paul had been sent in the night with a guard of soldiers to the governor's house in a distant city. Paul said to the governor: "I want to have my case tried in Rome before the emperor, for I am a Roman citizen!"

So Paul was sent as a prisoner to Rome on this sailing vessel. Some of his friends were with him. One was "the beloved physician," Doctor Luke, the man who tells this story in the Bible.

Out upon the great Mediterranean Sea the ship sailed until it came to a wharf where there was a large wheat ship sailing to Rome. Paul and the soldiers were put on board this ship. Counting the soldiers and passengers, there were two hundred seventy-six people in all.

Soon their troubles began. The wind was blowing the wrong way, so that they had to go

very slowly. But at last they came to Fair
Havens, where they stayed much too long,
Paul thought, for the stormy season of the
year had come.

Paul said, "You ought to stay here for the
winter," but the captain of the soldiers only
made fun of him. The weather just then
seemed good, so they pulled up the anchors,
hoisted the sails, and put out from Fair Havens.

Hardly had they started when a terrible
storm broke upon them, driving the ship far
off its course. Seeing that the ship was in
danger of breaking in two, they threw great
ropes around it to hold it together. Then they
lowered the sails and let the vessel drift. For
two weeks they were tossed and driven by the
storm, seeing neither sun nor stars.

One night God sent an angel to Paul to
tell him, "Fear not, Paul; you shall reach

Rome in safety, and God will save all in the ship with you."

Early in the morning, Paul said to the sailors and soldiers, "Be of good cheer, God will save you all."

They made fun of him, and

the ship drifted on until in the darkness of the night they found they were near some island. They quickly threw out four anchors to save themselves from being dashed on the rocks, and how they longed for the morning!

As soon as daylight came and they saw the land, some selfish sailors at the front of the ship, pretending to put out some more anchors, lowered the rowboat and were just

getting ready to row away to the land, thinking only of saving themselves. Paul saw their trick and cried out to the soldiers, "Look! Except these men abide in the ship, you yourselves cannot be saved!"

No one made fun of Paul then, but the soldiers ran and cut away the rope of the boat and let the boat fall into the sea and drift away.

After they had eaten food, they threw all their wheat overboard to lighten the ship. As that did not help, they decided to run the ship upon the shore, but the bow struck the beach, and the stern was broken to pieces by the fury of the waves.

Some of the soldiers cried, "Kill all the prisoners, lest they swim to the shore and escape."

But the captain of the soldiers, who had grown to think much of Paul, said, "No; let each man who can swim jump overboard and swim for the shore."

This they did, and others, including Paul and Doctor Luke, followed on planks and other floating things from the ship. And all escaped safe to the land. So Paul, the prisoner, was right; the ship was lost, but God had saved all the two hundred seventy-six men in the ship with him!

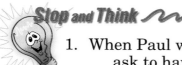

Stop and Think

1. When Paul was arrested, who did he ask to have try his case?

2. Name the friend that was traveling with Paul.

3. Who told Paul that he and the ship's crew would be safe in the storm?

The Bible Says,

"But whoso hearkeneth unto me shall dwell safely, and shall be quiet from fear of evil."

Proverbs 1:33

Word Watch

Greenbriar (grēn′brī·ər)
Appomattox (ăp·ə·măt′əks)
Confederate forces

cantered	gait	nicker
cavorted	girth	nuzzled
	bolt	

A Good Traveller

The gray colt was already famous in a small way when General Lee first saw him. Twice he had cantered off to the Greenbriar County Fair in what is now the state of West Virginia. And twice he had cantered around the track with two short blue ribbons fluttering from his bridle. When the crowds at the Fair cheered, he tossed his head proudly.

By the spring of 1861, the gray colt had grown into a handsome four-year-old, but no one had time any more to think about blue ribbons. He no longer grazed and sniffed the wind and kicked up his frisky heels in the hilly pasturelands of Greenbriar County. The North and South had gone to war, and his rider was a young Confederate major in a gray uniform.

Life was very pleasant in the Virginia army camp to which he had been taken. He was constantly being petted and praised by the soldiers. They admired his fine points— his easy gait, his proud carriage, his delicate ears and broad forehead, his full mane and tail. Then the gray horse would arch his neck and nicker softly.

One day he felt a strange hand on his mane. He turned his head and looked into the gentle dark eyes of a tall officer. There was a stir of excitement in the camp as the words, "General Lee is here," raced through the ranks.

General Robert E. Lee, the commander
of the Confederate forces, was the best-loved
man in the South. Every soldier wanted to
get a glimpse of him as he stood talking to
the officer who owned the gray horse.

"Major," said General Lee, "I shall need
that horse before the war is over." The handsome gray nuzzled the tall man's shoulder.
The General smiled as he
stroked the soft gray nose.

Sometimes it happens that way between
a man and a horse. It was love at first sight
between the General and the horse from

Greenbriar County. Whenever the General visited the camp, the gray horse would quiver with excitement at the touch of the gentle hand on his muzzle.

Several months passed before they saw each other again. The next time they met, it was in South Carolina. The horse had a new rider now, who wanted to present him as a gift to the beloved commander. General Lee refused the gift, but arranged to buy the animal which had attracted him so much.

"He is a good traveller," the General said, after he had ridden him a few times. The name stuck, and Traveller accompanied the army back to Virginia. He arched his proud neck as though he wanted everyone to understand that he carried the commander on his back. The winning of two blue ribbons was as nothing compared to the new honor which had come to him.

Traveller at War

At first Traveller was one of several horses which the General rode. But as one hard month followed another, soldiers in gray and in blue met in battle after battle. They fought and fell back and rushed forward to fight again. General Lee's other horses could not stand up under the strain.

But Traveller never faltered, no matter how long and difficult the march. In the fiercest battle, he did not bolt. But once, at least, he saved his master's life by becoming frightened at the bursting of a shell close by. He suddenly reared, and a shot passed under his girth, just missing the stirrup. Had Traveller been standing on the ground at that instant, his master might have been killed.

Usually, however, Traveller seemed as calm as his rider. The sight of the high-stepping gray horse carrying the General

never failed to inspire the men.
"Here comes Marse Robert on good old Traveller," they would say as commander and horse passed through the lines. Traveller would acknowledge the cheers by a toss of his graceful neck, and the men would laugh and cheer again.

The sight of the prancing horse inspired them even in battle. Once, when the Confederates were charging Fort Harrison, they fell back before heavy gunfire. The fort was an important one, and the commander urged them to try to storm it a second time. Once more a determined gray line surged forward. Once more it fell back.

Then General Lee rode up on Traveller, his dark eyes gleaming. He leaned forward in the saddle and urged them on with a wave of his sword.

"Try it again!" he shouted. "Try it again!"

"Even Traveller caught the spirit of his master," said one young soldier afterward. "He pranced and cavorted while the General was urging his men to make one more effort to take the fort." The soldiers drew fresh courage from that sight, and again they rushed forward. This time they were successful.

In the beginning of the war the South won most of the victories. But after two years the smart gray uniforms had worn out. The soldiers were in rags. Many were barefooted, and their feet were bleeding. They were weak from hunger.

Yet they still cheered when "good old Traveller" passed down the lines bearing General Lee. They scarcely ever saw one without the other now. During the last days of 1864, the gray horse was in constant use. Whenever possible, the General gave Traveller a chance to rest. But there were many days and nights when the saddle was not off his back.

The Battle Is Over

The time finally came when General Lee wrote General Grant, the Union commander, asking for terms of surrender. Never had the gray horse stepped more proudly than on that April day in 1865 when he carried General Lee toward Appomattox Courthouse, the little town where the two generals were to meet. It was as though the gray horse realized that his master was as great in defeat as he had been in victory.

Afterward, Traveller must have wondered at the strange scenes which took place. Men in tattered gray crowded around the horse and his rider. They tried to cheer, but the cheers ended in sobs. Some of them seemed to gain a little comfort from stroking Traveller's mane.

"Are we surrendered?" they asked.

The General nodded. "I have done the best I could. My heart is too full to say more."

The gray horse turned his head, as though in surprise. He whinnied softly.

After the war, General Lee became president of Washington College, in Lexington, Virginia. In Lexington the master and his horse had five peaceful years together. Every day they would go for a ride over the hilly roads.

The time came when the General could no longer take his daily ride. Sometimes he would gaze at the horse, his thoughts going back to the long marches, the cold nights and the bitter days, the noise and smoke of battle.

Then Traveller would whinny softly and nuzzle his master's shoulder. He, too, seemed to be remembering.

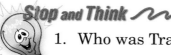

Stop and Think

1. Who was Traveller?

2. What was General Lee's job?

3. Who was fighting this war?

4. Name two ways that Traveller helped General Lee during the war.

5. What did General Lee do after Traveller carried him to the Appomattox Courthouse?

Word Watch

twined

glen: a narrow valley

chasm: a deep crack in the earth's surface

A Lost Lamb
a story from Scotland

There was never a sweeter child than dear little golden-haired Flora Campbell. Her footsteps were light as a rabbit's, her cheeks were like the June roses, her eyes were blue as the summer sky. Her heart was all sunshine. Her thoughts were as pure and fresh as the flowers which she twined in her hair.

She talked with the birds, the brooks, and the blossoms. And at sunrise every morning, when the shepherds went out with their flocks, you might hear her singing among the hills.

Everyone loved the gentle little child, for she was kind and good and fair.

It was evening among the hills. The sun had set, and it grew dark in the narrow valleys. One by one the stars appeared in the sky, sailing with the new moon among the summer clouds. The people in the cottages spread their tables for supper and lighted the lamps.

But where was Flora Campbell? She had never been so late coming home. Her grandfather went to the door a dozen times to look for her. "Have you see Flora?" he asked everyone who passed by.

How could he sit down to supper with Flora away? He looked up to the hills, his lips moving in prayer.

Flora's mother stood by the window as the last light of day faded away upon the mountains. Her lips moved, too: "Kind Father in Heaven, keep all harm from our dear lamb, and bring her safely home again."

Gaffer Campbell went out into the street, leaning on his staff. He knocked at every door, always asking the same question: "Have you seen my grandchild Flora?"

One man said that he had met her far up on the mountain gathering wildflowers.

"When was that?"

"It was near noon, I think."

Another man had seen her in the path that leads to the Moss Glen. She was sitting on a rock and making a willow basket for her grandfather. "That was early in the morning, I think."

Still another man had seen her. He had passed her near the head of the lake, only an hour before sunset, and she was carrying a basket of flowers on her arm.

"But where is she now?"

"We must go and find her at once!" cried several of the young men.

"Ah me, Gaffer Campbell!" said a white-haired old shepherd. "I was afraid that something was about to happen. The youngest lamb of my flock was lost in the hills today."

"Heaven grant that my little lamb may be safe!" said Gaffer Campbell.

Everybody in the village knew now that little Flora was lost. Soon the men were ready to go in search of her. Bright torches shone on the hilltops and in the valleys. Up

and down the mountain paths the young
men went, calling, "Flora! Flora!" But there
was no answer.

Gaffer Campbell leaned upon his staff.
He said not a word. He could not weep, for
his heart was too full. But Flora's mother sat
in her cottage, weeping and calling the name
of her child.

The village pastor came. He had heard
that Flora was missing, and he had come to
speak words of hope to her friends. "Do not
weep," he said. "Flora will be found."

But her mother still cried, "The child is
lost! the child is lost!"

"He who takes care of the lambs in the
winter storm will take care of your child,"
said the kind man.

Just then they heard a dog bark far
down in the deep valley called Moss Glen.
They saw the torches passing quickly toward

the same place. Gaffer Campbell and the
pastor started at once to the glen. But Flora's
mother passed them and ran wildly up the
narrow path. They looked down into the dark
glen. They could hear the dog very plainly now.

A little farther, and they came to the
edge of the steep chasm called the "Deer's
Mouth." Here the young men were standing
with their torches.
They were trying to
look down into the
chasm, but all was
dark there. They
could hear no
sound but the
quick, sharp
barking of the
dog, and that
seemed to be
far, far below them.

"We must go down!" cried one of the young men. "That is my dog Lad, and he knows Flora as well as I do."

"Yes, we must go down!" cried another. "Where are the ropes?"

Soon long ropes were brought. Strong men held them while Donald, Lad's young master, made ready to go down into the chasm. He took hold of a rope and swung himself from the edge of the rock. Down, down, he went. He could see the bright torches above him, but when he looked down there was only darkness.

At last Donald's feet touched the ground below. His dog ran to meet him. By the light of the torch which he held in his hand, he looked around him.

There on a thick bed of moss lay little Flora Campbell. She was holding in her arms the lost lamb.

Donald went close to her and looked at

her. Her eyes were shut. She was asleep. He
looked at the little lamb. Around one
of its legs, he saw a ribbon
from the child's hat.

Then he looked
up and called to his friends
above, "Flora's safe! Flora's safe!"

The sound awoke the little girl. She
looked around and saw the young man.

"Dear Donald," she said, "I am so glad
you have come! Now we can save your lamb."

The good people of the village soon
learned how it had all happened. Flora had
seen the young lamb fall into the chasm.
Looking over the edge of the rocks, she saw it
lying at the bottom of the Deer's Mouth.

She did not stop to think, but she began
at once to climb down to it. It was no easy
thing to do. Few men would have been brave
enough to try it.

But at last she was safe at the bottom.
She found that one of the lamb's legs was
broken, and she bound it up with the ribbon
of her hat. Then she held the little creature
in her arms till she fell asleep on the bed of
moss.

The people of the village were very
happy that night when they carried Flora
home. The child had never been so dear to
them before.

Donald's father gave her the lamb that she had saved. Often after that, Flora was seen playing on the hillside with her little pet, and everybody who met her spoke to her kindly and whispered, "May God bless the dear child!"

Stop and Think

1. Why were Flora's mother and grandfather upset one evening?

2. Besides the village people, Who did they ask for help?

3. Why had Flora gone down into the chasm?

The Lost Lamb

Storm upon the mountain,
　Rainy torrents beating,
And the little snow-white lamb
　Bleating, ever bleating!

Storm upon the mountain,
　Night upon its throne,
And the little snow-white lamb
　All alone, alone!

Down the road, the shepherd
　Drives his flock from far;
Through the cloud and falling rain,
　Shines no beacon star.

Fast he hurries homeward,
　Never hears the moan
Of the pretty snow-white lamb
　Left alone, alone!

At the shepherd's doorway
　Stands his little son,

Sees the sheep come running home,
  Counts them one by one.

He counts them full and fairly,
  And misses only one—
It is the little snow-white lamb,
  Left alone, alone.

Up the hills he races,
  Against the stormy wind,
Runs through fields and
    woodland,
  Leaves them all behind.

Storm upon the mountain,
  Night upon its throne,
There he finds the little lamb
  Left alone, alone.

Struggling, panting, sobbing,
  Falling on the ground,
Round the pretty creature's neck
  Both his arms are wound.

Soon upon his shoulders—
  All its bleating done—
home he carries the little lamb
  Left alone, alone!

King Canute (kə·nōot′)

alarmed

King Canute on the Seashore

A thousand years ago, there was a king of England named Canute. He was a good, brave king, and the people of his kingdom were always praising him.

"You are the greatest man who ever lived," one would say.

Then another would say, "O king! There can never be another man as mighty as you."

And another would say, "Great Canute, there is nothing in the world that dares to disobey you."

King Canute was a man of sense, and he grew very tired of hearing such foolish speeches. One day he was by the seashore, and many people were with him. They were praising him, as they were in the habit of doing. He thought that now he would teach them a lesson, and so he told them to set his chair on the beach close to the edge of the water.

"Am I the greatest man in the world?" he asked.

"O king!" they cried, "there is no one as mighty as you."

"Do all things obey me?" he asked.

"There is nothing that dares to disobey you, O king!" they said. "The world bows before you, and gives you honor."

"Will the sea obey me?" he asked; and he looked down at the little waves which were lapping the sand at his feet.

The foolish people were puzzled, but they did not dare say "No."

"Command it, O king! and it will obey," said one.

"Sea," cried King Canute, "I command you to come no farther! Waves, stop your rolling, and do not dare to touch my feet!"

But the tide came in, just as it always did. The water rose higher and higher. It came up around the king's chair and wet not only his feet, but also his robe. His people stood about him, alarmed, and wondering whether he had gone mad.

Then Canute rose to his feet, faced the crowd, and said, "My people, learn a lesson from what you have seen. There is only one King who is all-powerful; and it is He who rules the sea and holds the ocean in the hollow of His hand. It is He whom you ought to praise and serve above all others."

233

1. King Canute was the ruler of what country?

2. What habit did his people have that bothered King Canute?

3. What did King Canute use to teach his people a lesson?

4. What did King Canute command the sea to do? Did it?

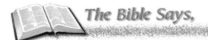

The Bible Says,

"The sea is His, and He made it: and His hands formed the dry land. O come, let us worship and bow down: let us kneel before the Lord our maker. For He is our God."

Psalm 95:5-7a

The Cricket in Times Square

"Psst!" he whispered. "Hey you up there—are you awake?"

There was no answer.

"Psst! Psst! Hey!" Tucker whispered again, louder this time.

From the shelf above came a scuffling,
like little feet feeling their way to the edge.
"Who is that going 'psst'?" said a voice.

"It's me," said Tucker. "Down here on the
stool."

A black head, with two shiny black eyes,
peered down at him. "Who are you?"

"A mouse," said Tucker. "Who are *you?*"

"I'm Chester Cricket," said the cricket. He
had a high, musical voice. Everything he said
seemed to be spoken to an unheard melody.

"My name's Tucker," said Tucker Mouse.
"Can I come up?"

"I guess so," said Chester Cricket. "This
isn't my house anyway."

Tucker jumped up beside the cricket and
looked him all over. "A cricket," he said admiringly.
"So you're a cricket. I never saw one before."

"I've seen mice before," the cricket said.
"I knew quite a few back in Connecticut."

236

"Is that where you're from?" asked Tucker.

"Yes," said Chester. "I guess I'll never see it again," he added wistfully.

"How did you get to New York?" asked Tucker Mouse.

"It's a long story," sighed the cricket.

"Tell me," said Tucker, settling back on his haunches. He loved to hear stories. It was almost as much fun as eavesdropping—if the story was true.

"Well it must have been two—no, three days ago," Chester Cricket began. "I was sitting on top of my stump, just enjoying the weather and thinking how nice it was that summer had started. I live inside an old tree stump, next to a willow tree, and I often go up to the roof to look around. And I'd been practicing jumping that day, too. On the other side of the stump from the willow tree there's a brook that runs past, and I'd been jumping back and forth across it to get my legs in condition for summer. I do a lot of jumping, you know."

"Me too," said Tucker Mouse. "Especially around the rush hour."

"And I had just finished jumping when I smelled something," Chester went on, "liverwurst, which I love."

"You like liverwurst?" Tucker broke in. "Wait! Wait! Just wait!"

In one leap, he sprang down all the way from the shelf to the floor and dashed over to his drainpipe. Chester shook his head as he watched him go. He thought Tucker was a very excitable person—even for a mouse.

Inside the drainpipe, Tucker's nest was a jumble of papers, scraps of cloth, buttons, lost jewelry, small change, and every- thing else that can be picked up in a subway station. Tucker tossed things left and right in a wild search. Neatness was not one of the things he aimed at in life. At last he dis- covered what he was looking for: a big piece of liverwurst he had found earlier that evening.

It was meant to be for breakfast tomorrow, but he decided that meeting his first cricket was a special occasion. Holding the liverwurst between his teeth, he whisked back to the newsstand.

"Look!" he said proudly, dropping the meat in front of Chester Cricket. "Liverwurst! You continue the story—we'll enjoy a snack too."

"That's very nice of you," said Chester. He was touched that a mouse he had known only a few minutes would share his food with him. "I had a little chocolate before, but besides that, nothing for three days."

"Eat! Eat!" said Tucker. He bit the liverwurst into two pieces and gave Chester the bigger one. "So you smelled the liverwurst—then what happened?"

"I hopped down from the stump and went off toward the smell," said Chester.

"Very logical," said Tucker Mouse, munching

with his cheeks full. "Exactly what I would have done."

"It was coming from a picnic basket," said Chester. "A couple of tuffets away from my stump the meadow begins, and there was a whole bunch of people having a picnic. They had hard boiled eggs, and cold roast chicken, and roast beef, and a whole lot of other things besides the liverwurst sandwiches, which I smelled."

Tucker Mouse moaned with pleasure at the thought of all that food.

"They were having such a good time laughing and singing songs that they didn't notice me when I jumped into the picnic basket," continued Chester. "I was sure they wouldn't mind if I had just a taste."

"Naturally not," said Tucker Mouse sympathetically. "Why mind? Plenty for all. Who could blame you?"

"Now I have to admit," Chester went on, "I had more than a taste. As a matter of fact, I ate so much that I couldn't keep my eyes open—what with being tired from the jumping and everything. And I fell asleep right there in the picnic basket. The first thing I knew, somebody had put a bag on top of me

that had the last of the roast beef sandwiches in it. I couldn't move!"

"Imagine!" Tucker exclaimed. "Trapped under roast beef sandwiches! Well, there are worse fates."

"At first I wasn't too frightened," said Chester. "After all, I thought, they probably come from New Canaan or some other nearby town. They'll have to unpack the basket sooner or later. Little did I know!" He shook his head and sighed. "I could feel the basket being carried into a car and riding somewhere and then being lifted down. That must have been the railroad station. Then I went up again and there was a rattling and roaring sound, the way a train makes. By this time I was pretty scared. I knew every minute was taking me further away from my stump, but there wasn't anything I could do. I was getting awfully cramped, too, under those roast beef sandwiches."

"Didn't you try to eat your way out?" asked Tucker.

"I didn't have any room," said Chester. "But every now and then the train would give a lurch and I managed to free myself a little. We traveled on and on, and then the train

stopped. I didn't have any idea where we were, but as soon as the basket was carried off, I could tell from the noise it must be New York."

"You never were here before?" Tucker asked.

"Goodness no!" said Chester. "But I've heard about it. There was a swallow I used to know who told about flying over New York every spring and fall on her way to the North and back. But what would I be doing here?" He shifted uneasily from one set of legs to another. "I'm a country cricket."

"Don't worry," said Tucker Mouse. "I'll feed you liverwurst. You'll be all right. Go on with the story."

"It's almost over," said Chester. "The people got off one train and walked a ways and got on another—even noisier than the first."

"Must have been the subway," said Tucker.

"I guess so," Chester Cricket said. "You

can imagine how scared I was. I didn't know *where* I was going! For all I knew they could have been heading for Texas, although I don't guess many people from Texas come all the way to Connecticut for a picnic."

"It could happen," said Tucker, nodding his head.

"Anyway I worked furiously to get loose. And finally I made it. When they got off the second train, I took a flying leap and landed in a pile of dirt over in the corner of this place where we are."

"Such an introduction to New York," said Tucker, "to land in a pile of dirt in Times Square subway station. Tsk, tsk, tsk."

"And here I am," Chester concluded forlornly. "I've been lying over there for three days not knowing what to do. At last I got so nervous I began to chirp."

"That was the sound!" interrupted Tucker Mouse. "I heard it, but I didn't know what it was."

"Yes, that was me," said Chester. "Usually I don't chirp until later on in the summer—but my goodness, I had to do *something!*"

The cricket had been sitting next to the edge of the shelf. For some reason—perhaps it was a faint noise, like padded feet tiptoeing across the floor—he happened to look down. A shadowy form that had been crouching silently below in the darkness made a spring and landed right next to Tucker and Chester.

"Watch out!" Chester shouted, "A cat!" He dove headfirst into the matchbox.

Chester buried his head in the Kleenex. He didn't want to see his new friend, Tucker Mouse, get killed. Back in Connecticut he

246

had sometimes watched the one-sided fights of cats and mice in the meadow, and unless the mice were near their holes, the fights always ended in the same way. But this cat had been upon them too quickly: Tucker couldn't have escaped.

There wasn't a sound. Chester lifted his head and very cautiously looked behind him. The cat—a huge tiger cat with gray-green and black stripes along his body—was sitting on his hind legs, switching his tail around his forepaws. And directly between those fore-paws, in the very jaws of his enemy, sat Tucker Mouse. He was watching Chester curiously. The cricket began to make frantic signs that the mouse should look up and see what was looming over him.

Very casually Tucker raised his head. The cat looked straight down on him. "Oh him," said Tucker, chucking the cat under the

chin with his right front paw, "he's my best friend. Come out from the matchbox."

Chester crept out, looking first at one, then the other.

"Chester, meet Harry Cat," said Tucker. "Harry, this is Chester. He's a cricket."

"I'm very pleased to make your acquaintance," said Harry Cat in a silky voice.

Follow the amazing adventures of Chester Cricket, Tucker Mouse, and Harry Cat in the book, *The Cricket in Times Square*.

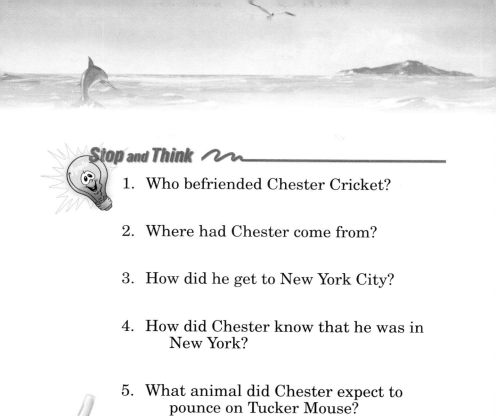

1. Who befriended Chester Cricket?

2. Where had Chester come from?

3. How did he get to New York City?

4. How did Chester know that he was in New York?

5. What animal did Chester expect to pounce on Tucker Mouse?

Who Taught Them?

Who taught the bird to build
    her nest
  Of wool, and hay, and moss?
Who taught her how to weave
    it best,
  And lay the twigs across?

        Who taught the busy bee to
          fly
          Among the sweetest flowers,
        And lay her store of honey
          by
        To eat in winter hours?

Who taught the little ant the
    way
  The narrow hole to bore,
And through the pleasant
    summer day
  To gather up her store?

        'Twas God who taught them
          all the way,
          And gave their little skill,
        And teaches children, if they
          pray,
        To do His holy will.

                  —*Albert N. Raub*

Word
Watch

harness   professor

familiar   pierce

rearranging

immediately

awl: a small, pointed tool for making
holes in leather or wood

All Because of an Awl

One cold, wintry morning, another son
was born at the home of the village harness
maker. "I am the best harness maker in
France," said Mr. Braille, "but Louis will not
be a harness maker. Our son, Louis, shall be
a professor!"

As Louis grew, his sparkling blue eyes
missed nothing, and he found many interesting things for a boy to do. Louis especially
liked the times he spent playing in the harness shop while his father was working.

His father gave him scraps of leather, which the little boy enjoyed arranging and re-arranging. Sometimes he pretended they were cows in a pasture. Other times they were soldiers marching in straight lines.

One bright summer day when Louis was three years old, he was busy playing with his scraps of leather. He wanted to make a harness like his father's. He stepped over to his father's bench and took a little awl—a long, pointed tool that he was forbidden to play with.

Louis tried to punch a hole in a scrap of leather, but the leather was tough, and the awl would not go through. Louis pushed harder. The awl slipped—and pierced his eye.

Louis's injured eye became infected. Then things began to look blurry through his other eye. One morning Louis could hear the birds singing outside while it was still dark. It would always be dark for Louis now. He was blind.

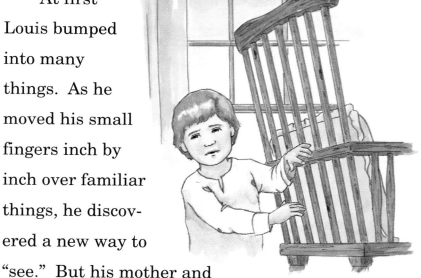

At first Louis bumped into many things. As he moved his small fingers inch by inch over familiar things, he discovered a new way to "see." But his mother and father knew he could never read books. He could never become a professor.

When Louis was five years old, a new pastor moved to the village. That was the beginning of a strong friendship. Louis spent many hours listening to his new friend tell stories. Through these stories, Louis learned

about the stars, the many animals, and how plants grow. He also listened to stories about kindness, obedience, and courage—stories Louis would never forget.

At the age of seven, Louis walked every morning to the village school with his cousin. Louis was soon at the top of most of his classes. In arithmetic, he often could work a problem in his head as fast as the other students could work it on paper. But during reading and writing, Louis had nothing to do. "Are there no books for me to read?" he asked sadly.

When he was ten years old, Louis left the village to go to a school for blind children. He was going to learn to read! But again he was disappointed. The reading was from books that had raised print. Each letter was raised from the page so that it could be felt with the fingers. Each letter was so large that only a few words could fit on a page. By the time Louis had figured out all of the letters, he often had forgotten the beginning of the sentence.

"We need a better way to read," said Louis. He could think of nothing else. He tried many times to figure out an alphabet code, but each time he failed. "Will I never be able to read books for myself?"

"Only God knows the answer," replied Louis's pastor. "Trust Him."

One day a captain in the army came to the school. He told how he could send secret messages at night by making dots and dashes on paper.

"This is it!" thought Louis. "I can make an alphabet code with dots!"

Louis worked every spare minute on the new alphabet. Everywhere he went he had paper and a dull awl for punching dots.

He made six dots. Then he made every
letter from these same six dots.

Braille Alphabet						
A	B	C	D	E	F	G
H	I	J	K	L	M	N
O	P	Q	R	S	T	U
V	W	X	Y	Z		

"It works!" cried Louis one summer day as he ran his finger over the six-dot alphabet. "It's so simple, but it works!"

And it did work. Louis made copies of the alphabet to take back to school. The students were eager to learn this new six-dot alphabet. One boy was quiet for a long time. Then he said, "I have written a sentence. Can you read it?"

I __ __ __ __ __ __ __ __ __.

The students began immediately to write down everything the teachers taught them "We can remember so much more!" they told Louis.

About five years later, Louis was asked to stay at the school for the blind—not as a student, but as a professor!

Because of a sharp awl, Louis became blind. He could not read or write. Because of a dull awl, many blind people are now able to read and write. The way of writing for the blind that Louis Braille invented is named after him. It is called Braille.

Stop and Think

1. What did Louis's father want him to become?

2. What is an awl?

3. What was the result of Louis's accident with the awl?

4. When Louis was a child, how were blind children taught to read?

5. What idea did Louis have after he heard an army captain speak?

6. What is this new way of reading called today?

Kitten-in-a-Basket

Long ago, when America was young, there was a little spotted kitten named Nelly. She had extra toes on her front paws and very pretty manners.

During her first weeks Nelly lived on a farm in a state called Pennsylvania. In the spring she noticed that everyone seemed very busy. A lot of people came and took off most of the furniture and the pigs and the cattle. At last only the four horses, the dog, one cow, a bull calf and Nelly were left.

Then, one morning at dawn, the young farmer and his wife rose up and packed everything they still owned on three of the horses. On the white mare they put a sort of saddle between two crates of chickens. The little girl, Hannah, and her mother took turns riding at the head of the procession on this horse, which wore a bell around her neck. Wherever the bell-mare went, the other three horses would follow. In front of

the horses went the young farmer, with his
gun over his arm. He and the dog drove the
cow and the calf before them up the trail.

As for Nelly, she saw all this through the
cracks in the basket in which she traveled,
sometimes in Hannah's lap and sometimes in
the lap of Hannah's mother. At first she
mewed and mewed with fright.

"Got to get rid of that yowling kitten,"
the farmer said. "Turn her loose, Hannah.
She can still find her way to the
settlements."

But Hannah begged hard and said that
she was sure that Nelly would soon quiet
down. And Nelly did. She even came to like
the rocking of the horse, and the smell of new
country which came to her through the cracks
of her basket. Often, when the family
stopped to rest, she was let out and given
warm milk to drink. She had no home any
more, and cats love their homes. But soon
Nelly adopted her basket as home. When
Hannah called, she would jump in and settle
down in a contented ball of fur and whiskers.

At night they sometimes slept in houses
and sometimes beside the trail under the
stars. Then Nelly snuggled close to Hannah
when she heard the wolves howl. Every day
they moved farther and farther west. At
night, their meals were cooked over a fire
beside the trail. The young farmer shot
squirrels and rabbits. His wife cooked them

in an iron pot which one of the horses carried. She made hoe cakes of corn meal close to the embers. Always there was milk. They moved slowly, in one direction, and even the kitten-in-the-basket enjoyed the life.

At last the trail began to climb up and up and up, among rocks, past loud water-falls. At first all the animals were terrified, but after a while they became used to the mountains. Now there were almost no houses. When Nelly woke in the night, she sometimes saw that Hannah's father was sitting, listening, with his gun across his lap.

Once they met a family coming in the opposite direction.

The horses stopped and the two men talked.

"Don't go on to Kentucky," the stranger said. "There are too many Indians. Too many settlers are being killed. We had land there and a cabin built last fall. But we are coming back, where we can sleep at nights without being afraid."

"The land is good?" asked Hannah's father.

"Yes, but it is dark with blood."

Hannah's father glanced at her mother. She held her head up and smiled back at him.

"We're going on," he said.

So the two families parted on the trail.

After a while, Hannah's father and mother took turns sitting up with the gun, every night.

"Go to sleep, Hannah," they said. "We want to scare off any bears that might come to call on the kitten. Bears are so tame in these woods that they want to be invited for supper."

Hannah laughed. With her father and mother so near, she wasn't afraid. But Nelly crawled right up under Hannah's chin, and so they went to sleep.

After a while the trail began to wind down hill.

Beyond them they could see a great valley, partly forested and partly open.

"Daniel Boone's country," said Hannah's father. "We'll be at the fort soon. We'll settle somewhere near neighbors. The land is the best in America, they say."

But now he walked ahead of the cow and the calf, with his gun cradled on his arm. He looked to right and to left as he walked, trying to see into the shadows, to study every turn of the trail.

When the Indians Came

Yet when the Indians came, his gun was leaning against a tree a little way off and he was eating the drumstick of a wild turkey which he had shot a few days before. It was noonday, with the sun overhead—such a quiet, peaceful noonday.

There were four Indians, with paint on their faces and feathers in their hair, and long leather leggings. They came between the man and his gun. They looked at him and at the woman and the little girl. The dog growled, but Hannah's father ordered him to be quiet.

He smiled at the Indians and made signs of friendship. He invited them to eat turkey with him. They squatted down and ate, but always they kept between him and the gun. When they laughed, it was to each other. Were they friendly, or did they mean trouble? It was hard to say.

Hannah had an idea. She took the basket in which Nelly was napping, and undid the catch which held the cover down. Then she pushed it into the center of the circle. "Here kitty, kitty," she called softly.

For a moment Nelly didn't stir. Then the top of the basket rose a little and Nelly's face appeared, peeking out. She had a round head and eyes of kitten-blue. The Indians had never seen a cat or a kitten before. They stared at the little round face. Pretty soon Nelly squirmed out of the basket and Hannah took a stick and played with her.

Nelly had never played so prettily. In no time at all the Indians were laughing with pleasure. They, too, took sticks and played with Nelly, and Nelly played with them. Then the man who appeared to be their chief rose, picked Nelly up, and held her on his bare arm. He nodded and smiled. The others, too, rose.

They all made signs of friendship. The chief
found an English word.

"Good," he said, and then he repeated,
"Good."

"He's taking Nelly!" cried Hannah.

"Let him," her father said quickly. "We
don't dare anger him."

"Indeed, he *shan't* take Nelly!" Hannah cried. She ran up to the Indian and pulled Nelly away from him. Then she faced him, her eyes sparkling and her cheeks red.

The Indians looked at her in surprise. Suddenly the chief laughed. He liked her courage.

"Good," he said again. "Good." And he and the others went off.

But another day the Indians came back, bringing deer meat. And once again they suddenly appeared when the horses were floundering in a swamp and Hannah's father needed help.

They were true friends to all Hannah's family, then and later when their cabin was built. But Hannah was their favorite. Hannah and her kitten, the kitten who had come to Kentucky in a basket. And later on, some of Nelly's own kittens went to live in the Indian camp. All the Indian children made a

great fuss over them, and treated them as something very rare and wonderful.

1. Where was Nelly's family going as they moved west?

2. Name the animals that they took with them.

3. Why was the family they met on the road leaving Kentucky and going back where they had come from?

4. How could Hannah's father tell that his wife wanted to go on to Kentucky?

5. What was the main reason that the Indians became their friends?

sixpence   forlorn   obliged

continuously   fourpenny

ravenous   devour

currant: a small raisin-like fruit
makeweight: anything added to a scale to bring
it up to the desired weight

Suppose

from *A Little Princess*

For several days it had rained continuously; the streets were chilly and sloppy and full of dreary, cold mist. There was mud everywhere—sticky London mud—and over everything lay drizzle and fog. There were several long and tiresome errands to be done, and Sara was sent out again and again, until her shabby clothes were damp through. Besides all this, she had had no dinner. She was so cold and hungry and tired that her face began to have a pinched look. Now and then some kind-hearted person passing her in the street glanced at her with sudden sympathy, but she did not know that.

She hurried on, trying to make her mind think of something else. It was really very necessary. Her way of doing it was to "pretend" and "suppose" with all the strength that was left in her.

"Suppose I had dry clothes on," she thought. "Suppose I had good shoes and a long, thick coat and fine woolen stockings and a whole umbrella. And suppose—suppose— just when I was near a baker's where they sold hot buns, I should find sixpence—which belonged to nobody. *Suppose,* if I did, I should go into the shop and buy six of the hottest buns and eat them all without stopping."

Some very odd things happen in this world sometimes.

It certainly was an odd thing that happened to Sara. She had to cross the street just when she was saying this to herself. The mud was dreadful—she almost had to wade. In picking her way, she had to look down at her feet and the mud, and in looking down— just as she reached the pavement—she saw something shining in the gutter. It was actually a piece of silver—a tiny piece trodden upon by many feet, but still with spirit enough left to shine a little.

Not quite a sixpence, but the next thing to it—a fourpenny piece.

In one second it was in her cold little red-and-blue hand.

"Oh," she gasped, "it is true! It is true!"

And then, if you will believe me, she looked straight at the shop directly facing her.

And it was a baker's shop, and a cheerful, stout, motherly woman with rosy cheeks was putting into the window a tray of delicious newly baked hot buns, fresh from the oven—large, plump, shiny buns, with currants in them.

It almost made Sara feel faint for a few seconds—the shock, and the sight of the buns, and the delightful odors of warm bread floating up through the baker's cellar window.

She knew she need not hesitate to use the little piece of money. It had evidently been lying in the mud for some time, and its owner was completely lost in the stream of passing people who crowded and jostled each other all day long.

"But I'll go and ask the baker woman if she has lost anything," she said to herself, rather faintly. So she crossed the pavement and put her wet foot on the step. As she did so she saw something that made her stop.

It was a little figure more forlorn even than herself—a little figure which was not much more than a bundle of rags from which small, bare, red muddy feet peeped out.

Above the rags appeared a head of tangled hair and a dirty face with big, hollow, hungry eyes.

Sara knew they were hungry eyes the moment she saw them, and she felt a sudden sympathy. The child stared up at Sara and shuffled herself aside a little, so as to give her room to pass. She was used to being made to give room to everybody. She knew that if a policeman chanced to see her he would tell her to "move on."

Sara clutched her little fourpenny piece

and hesitated for a few seconds. Then she spoke to her.

"Are you hungry?" she asked.

"Ain't I jist?" she said in a hoarse voice. "Jist ain't I?"

"Haven't you had any dinner?" said Sara.

"No dinner," more hoarsely still and with more shuffling. "Nor yet no bre'fast—nor yet no supper. No nothin'."

"Since when?" asked Sara.

"Dunno. Never got nothin' today—no-where. I've axed and axed."

"Wait a minute," Sara said to the beggar child.

She went into the shop. It was warm and smelled deliciously. The woman was just going to put some more hot buns into the window.

"If you please," said Sara, "have you lost

fourpence—a silver fourpence?" And she held the forlorn little piece of money out to her.

The woman looked at it and then at her—at her intense little face and draggled, once fine clothes.

"Bless us, no," she answered. "Did you find it?"

"Yes," said Sara. "In the gutter."

"Keep it, then," said the woman. "It may have been there for a week, and goodness knows who lost it. *You* could never find out."

"I know that," said Sara, "but I thought I would ask you."

"Not many would," said the woman, looking puzzled and interested and good-natured all at once.

"Do you want to buy something?" she added, as she saw Sara glance at the buns.

"Four buns, if you please," said Sara. "Those at a penny each."

The woman went to the window and put some into a paper bag.

Sara noticed that she put in six.

"I said four, if you please," she explained. "I have only fourpence."

"I'll throw in two for makeweight," said the woman with her good-natured look. "I dare say you can eat them sometime. Aren't you hungry?"

A mist rose before Sara's eyes.

"Yes," she answered. "I am very hungry, and I am much obliged to you for your kindness; and" —she was going to add—"there is a child outside who is hungrier than I am." But just at that moment two or three customers came in at once, and each one seemed in a hurry, so she could only thank the woman again and go out.

The beggar girl was still huddled up in the corner of the step. She looked frightful in her wet and dirty rags. She was staring straight before her with a look of suffering, and Sara saw her suddenly draw the back of her hand across her eyes to rub away tears. She was muttering to herself.

Sara opened the paper bag and took out one of the hot buns, which had already warmed her own cold hands a little.

"See," she said, putting the bun in the ragged lap, "this is nice and hot. Eat it, and you will not feel so hungry."

The child started and stared up at her, as if such sudden, amazing good luck almost frightened her; then she snatched up the bun and began to cram it into her mouth with great wolfish bites.

"Oh my! Oh, my!" Sara heard her say hoarsely, in wild delight. *"Oh, my!"*

Sara took out three more buns and put them down.

The sound in the hoarse, ravenous voice was awful.

"She is hungrier than I am," she said to herself. "She's starving." But her hand trembled when she put down the fourth bun. "I'm not starving," she said—and she put down the fifth.

The child was still snatching and devouring when Sara turned away. She was too ravenous to give any thanks, even if she had ever been taught politeness—which she had not.

"Good-by," said Sara.

When she reached the other side of the street, she looked back. The child had a bun in each hand and had stopped in the middle of a bite to watch her. Sara gave her a little nod, and the child jerked her shaggy head in response, and until Sara was out of sight she did not take another bite or even finish the one she had begun.

At that moment the baker-woman looked out of her shop window.

"Well, I never!" she exclaimed. "If that young un hasn't given her buns to a beggar child! It wasn't because she didn't want them, either. Well, well, she looked hungry enough. I'd give something to know what she did it for."

She stood behind her window for a few moments and pondered. Then her curiosity got the better of her. She went to the door and spoke to the beggar child.

"Who gave you those buns?" she asked her.

The child nodded her head toward Sara's vanishing figure.

"What did she say?" inquired the woman.

"Axed me if I was 'ungry," replied the hoarse voice.

"What did you say?"

"Said I was jist."

"And then she came in and got the buns, and gave them to you, did she?"

The child nodded.

"How many?"

"Five."

The woman thought it over.

"Left just one for herself," she said in a low voice. "And she could have eaten the whole six—I saw it in her eyes."

She looked after the little draggled far-away figure and felt more disturbed in her usually comfortable mind than she had felt for many a day.

"I wish she hadn't gone so quick," she said. "Bless my bones if she shouldn't have had a dozen." Then she turned to the child.

"Are you hungry yet?" she said.

"I'm allus hungry," was the answer, "but 't ain't as bad as it was."

"Come in here," said the woman, and she held open the shop door.

The child got up and shuffled in. To be invited into a warm place full of bread seemed an incredible thing. She did not know what was going to happen. She did not care, even.

"Get yourself warm," said the woman, pointing to a fire in the tiny back room. "And look here; when you are hard up for a bit of bread, you can come in here and ask for it. Bless my bones if I won't give it to you for that young one's sake."

Read the entire book, *A Little Princess,* by Frances Hodgson Burnett for the complete story of Sara's adventures.

Stop and Think

1. How many of the things that Sara "supposed" actually came true?

2. How did Sara show that she was honest?

3. Why did the woman give Sara two extra buns?

ferry   pewter

gourds   Golden Pippins

russet   reassured orchardman

comb of honey quinces   acres

Lost in the Apple Cave

Swinging her worn shoes from the steps of the covered wagon whose great canvas top had been her only roof for months, Rose looked back along the wilderness road. At its beginning lay the mountains. The road ended at a wide river.

Rose and her father and mother were on their way from New England to that great unknown place beyond the Ohio River called the West. Everything they owned was packed in the great lumbering wagon, camped now on the banks of the Ohio until a flatboat should come to ferry it across.

The big wagon was like home to the twelve-year-old girl. In a corner crowded with pewter plates, patchwork quilts, sacks of cornmeal, and gourds of milk, Rose had a family of dolls made of great pine cones. She had dressed them in bits of her own calico dress as it had become torn. The little heads of these dolls, made of small wild apples, wore sunbonnets like Rose's own.

Kicking her heels against the wagon step, Rose wished that she knew what lay within those deep woods at the right of their camp. She watched her mother bending over some knitting. Her father was trying to catch fish for supper. Rose stood up at last, swinging a little handmade basket over her arm.

"I am going for a walk, Mother," she said. "Perhaps I can find some berries in the wood to eat with our porridge tonight."

"Do not go too far, Rose," her mother warned. "Your father saw a big brown bear quite close this morning."

"I will be back by supper time," Rose said.

In five minutes Rose was out of all sight and sound of the wagon camp.

The faint stir of a passing snake among the fallen leaves in the forest, the patter of a chipmunk's little feet, the flapping of a crow's wings were the only sounds. Rose had never thought that she could lose the trail. But soon it seemed as if each moment she were going deeper into the wilderness. Her arms and legs were scratched by the bushes.

In the Cave

Rose ran. She clung to the little rush basket for comfort. It broke her fall as she stepped down, tumbled, and found herself a prisoner in a cave. The opening had been carefully screened by leafy branches and bushes. When she picked herself up and looked about, Rose could not believe her eyes.

The cave smelled deliciously of apples. Eating apples were a new fruit in those days, and rather rare. But here, in a roomy cave with a little bubbling spring at the back to keep the fruit moist, were shelves and shelves of wonderful apples, stored away for the winter. There were August apples. There were great Golden Pippins, hard little russet apples, and great red spicy apples. Choosing one of these apples, Rose sat down on the mossy floor to munch it. This might be a bear's cave, she thought, but it was a pleasant place.

Rose ate her apple down to its nest of big black seeds. She was just cupping her hands to drink from the spring, when a shadow darkened the door of the cave. Could it be the bear? Rose was frightened as she saw a dark form closing the opening. But a voice reassured her.

"Don't be afraid, little girl. It's only Appleseed Johnny. Welcome to my orchard!"

The man—strange indeed with his long hair, ragged clothes, and feet bare save for Indian moccasins—held out his hand to Rose.

"Come and see my trees, little girl," he said. "Come and see my house, too. Then I will show you the way to the camp again."

The man led Rose out of the cave and into a clearing where grew apple, cherry, peach, and plum trees.

He was still a young man, but he said that he had traveled on foot to Pittsburgh all the long way from Springfield, in Massachusetts.

His name was John Chapman. He was called Appleseed Johnny because he was the only orchardman of the pioneers. He loved apples, and he knew how much the West needed fruit.

Appleseed Johnny showed Rose the shed where he sorted and washed apple seeds and started new trees. Then they went into the cabin he had built for himself of logs of oak, chestnut, and pine. The nails in the cedar door were handmade. So was the star-shaped iron latch.

In the light of the big stone fireplace, the girl thought that Appleseed Johnny looked like an Indian—as brown, sharp-eyed, and slender. He gave a low call. Down from the shelf near the roof fluttered a sleepy little owl to nestle on his shoulder.

"Folks say there are bears in these woods," said Rose.

Appleseed Johnny laughed. He went to the door and made an odd growling sound. Wide-eyed, Rose saw a shaggy brown animal lumber out of the gathering darkness, sniff at Appleseed Johnny, and then pass by.

Appleseed Johnny filled a big pewter mug with milk for Rose. He put a comb of golden honey and three red apples in her basket. Last, he gave her a little apple tree, no taller than her pine-cone doll, and a small deerskin bag of seeds.

"Now I will lead you to the edge of the woods," he said. "And when you come to your new home in the wilderness, set out this young apple tree in the sunshine. Water it.

Build a little fence of brush about it to keep off the deer.

"In this bag are seeds of other apples, of berries, pears, cherries, grapes, plums, and peaches. Plant them and take care of them. Your mother will want berries and fruits for her pies, and jellies and jams for the winter. Your new home in the West will need grape-vines growing over it, and a pink cloud of orchard blossoms in the spring."

As Appleseed Johnny talked, he led Rose safely through the darkening forest until she could see her own campfire and smell the fish her mother was cooking.

"Goodbye, and thank you," she said.

"Goodbye, Little Pioneer," he said. "Re-member Appleseed Johnny and plant your trees."

"I will!" she called, as she ran over to hide her little tree and the seeds.

A flatboat was waiting for them in the morning. They drifted, wagon and all, over the Ohio River. Rose's covered wagon rolled on through the unsettled, wild country of Ohio. On, on went the wagon, until Rose's father found a farm site.

The seasons passed quickly. The land was cleared and a cabin built in two years. That was the year that Rose picked berries from the bushes that grew from Appleseed Johnny's seeds. In four years, roads were built, the cabin made larger, and Rose's dresses were longer. That was the year she first picked peaches, cherries, and plums from the trees planted from Appleseed Johnny's seeds.

In six years, Rose was a young lady. It was another October. The apples from Appleseed Johnny's little tree were in the kitchen, to be made into apple butter for the winter.

On linen thread, hanging from the beams of the kitchen, were strips of apples drying. The crane in the open fireplace held a brass kettle filled with peeled apples, with quinces and molasses added for flavor.

Rose would spend days preserving the apples. Down cellar, tubs of applesauce would freeze and keep through the winter as sweet as when it was made. The dried apples would be made into pies.

Appleseed Johnny Again

Rose stirred the apple butter, her back to the open door. Suddenly she heard a low call, like that of a little screech owl. Turning, she saw a surprising figure.

The man was as tall and straight as an Indian, and as keen-eyed. On his back he carried a great sack.

He was as ragged as a beggar, and his hair had grown to his shoulders. He smiled at Rose. "You have grown, my child," he said.

"Appleseed Johnny!" she cried.

"Yes, I am Appleseed Johnny, still planting orchards in the wilderness. I gave away my house, and have been wandering for many years, scattering seeds, and teaching the pioneers how to plant and care for orchards."

"Come in," Rose begged. "Spend the night with us. These are your apples I am cooking. Your tree lived. Your seeds grew and gave us fruit."

An old letter tells us the rest of the story: how Appleseed Johnny spent the night in the cabin, made welcome by Roselle Rice and her family. In the morning he started on again. He carried a Bible in the sack with his seeds, and left one leaf of it with Rose. Then he tramped off into the woods farther West. She never saw him again.

Many covered-wagon children knew Appleseed Johnny, though Rose was the only one who wrote about him. But Appleseed Johnny walked for forty years, leaving at lonely cabins his little deerskin bags of seeds and his Bible pages. He planted the orchards that now cover acres of the West.

Following the trail he started, great freight trains return now to the East carrying barrels of Jonathan, Winesap, Spitzenburg, Northern Spy, Delicious, King, Greening, and Golden Pippin apples for hungry boys and girls. The sturdy covered-wagon people, going West, gave this region its cities, its farms, its schools. And every pink apple

blossom of the spring is scented with Appleseed Johnny's kindness to little Rose. Every bite of a rosy October apple tastes as sweet as those he laid away in his cave.

Stop and Think

1. Where were Rose and her family headed at the beginning of this story?

2. Why did Rose's mother tell her not to go too far on her walk?

3. Name the different kinds of apples Rose found in the cave.

4. What gifts did Appleseed Johnny give to Rose?

5. When and where did Rose see Appleseed Johnny again?

6. Besides planting apple orchards and giving seeds to the pioneers, what else did Appleseed Johnny give to the settlers?

buccaneering bee: a robber bee

The Rain Song

It isn't raining rain to me,
  It's raining daffodils;
In every dimpled drop I see
  Wild flowers on the hills;
The clouds of gray engulf the day
  And overwhelm the town;
It isn't raining rain to me,
  It's raining roses down.

It isn't raining rain to me,
  But fields of clover bloom,
Where every buccaneering bee
  May find a bed and room;
A health unto the happy!
  A fig for him who frets!
It isn't raining rain to me,
  It's raining violets.

—*Robert Loveman*

301

Word Watch

valuable   downcast

broilers   antiques

andirons   urn   sauntered

immediately   carriage lamp

Any Old Junk Today?

Never a week went by without Eddie's bringing home some piece of what Eddie called "valuable property," and his father called "junk."

The family always knew when Eddie had brought home a new treasure. Eddie would always announce at dinner, "I had a very enjoyable day today." When Eddie said this, his father would look at his mother and say, "Uh! Oh!"

After dinner, his father would go down to the basement. There he would find another piece of junk added to Eddie's collection.

"Now see here, Edward!" said his father one evening. "This junk collecting has

reached the limit. I am tired of it. The basement looks like a junk shop, or worse. This thing has got to stop."

Eddie looked very downcast. "But, Pop!" said Eddie. "It's my valuable property."

"Valuable property!" exclaimed his father. "Junk!"

The following Saturday, Rudy and the twins went on a hike with some of the boys in Rudy's class. Eddie wanted to go, too, but they said that he was too little. He felt very bad until his mother said that he could go with her and his father. They were driving out into the country to see if they could buy an old table.

It was a beautiful day. As they drove along the roads, Eddie saw the cows and the horses on the farms. He saw men working in the fields. He read the signs along the road. FRESH EGGS. BROILERS.

They had been driving for about an hour when Mr. Wilson brought the car to a stop in front of a store. There was a large sign hanging outside which Eddie could not read. "What does that sign say, Pop?" asked Eddie.

"It says ANTIQUES," said his father.

"Are we going to see Aunt Teek?" asked Eddie. "Does she own the store?"

"Not Aunt Teek," said his father. "Antiques. *Antique* means old. It means that the shop sells old things."

"You mean junk?" said Eddie.

"No, indeed!" said his father. "These things are valuable."

Mr. and Mrs. Wilson and Eddie walked up the path to the porch. The porch was full of all kinds of objects. Among them were some huge kettles, some fire screens, and brass and iron andirons. There were long iron forks, and tongs for handling the logs in a fireplace.

"Oh!" said Eddie, "It sure looks like junk."

All the windows were filled with shelves. The shelves were covered with glass vases, cups, plates, pitchers, and sugar bowls. The inside of the store was stuffed with tables, chairs, chests of drawers, and cabinets full of china.

"Hmmm," thought Eddie. "I'll bet a fellow could find some very valuable property around here."

While his father and Mother were talking to the owner of the shop, Eddie looked over the shelves. He peered into open boxes and barrels. Finally, he went through a doorway into a storeroom. There he came upon a man opening a barrel.

"Hello, son!" said the man. "Can I do something for you?"

"I'm just looking around," said Eddie.

In a moment, Eddie's eyes fell upon something that interested him very much indeed. On a shelf stood an old carriage lamp. It was rusty and covered with dust.

"Do you want to sell that lamp?" Eddie asked the man who was opening the barrel.

The man looked up. "I guess we do."

"How much is it?" asked Eddie.

"Oh, 'bout a quarter," said the man.

Eddie reached into his pocket and pulled out all his money. He had seventy-five cents.

"Okay!" said Eddie, briskly, "I'll take it."

The man took the lamp from the shelf. Just then, Eddie's eye fell upon another interesting object. It looked like a small iron urn with a wheel on each side. It, too, was rusty.

"What is that?" asked Eddie.

"Oh, that?" asked the man, lifting it down. "That's an old-fashioned coffee grinder."

"Those wheels are super!" said Eddie, his eyes very big. "How much is that?"

"Oh, I guess I can let you have that for fifty cents," said the man.

Eddie looked at the coffee grinder. Then he said, "I'll take that, too."

"Want them wrapped?" asked the man.

"Yes, please," replied Eddie.

He watched the man put the coffee grinder and lamp into a cardboard box. When he folded over the flaps, they didn't close because the end of the lamp was too long. The man tied a piece of cord over the top to hold the flaps down, but the end of the lamp still showed.

"I guess that will do," he said.

"Oh, sure!" replied Eddie, as he handed over his seventy-five cents. "That will do."

Eddie decided to go out the back door with his package. He ran to the car. He thought it would be best to put the package in the trunk of the car. His father had left the keys in the car, so Eddie unlocked the trunk. He placed the package on the shelf. Then he locked the trunk and put the keys in his pocket.

Some Valuable Property

Eddie sauntered back to the front porch. He was looking at a broken lock when his father and mother came out.

"Look, Pop," said Eddie. "This is a swell lock."

"It's a piece of junk," said Mr. Wilson. "No more junk is going into our house, Eddie. Put it down."

Eddie put the lock down and walked to the car with his father and mother. "You left the keys in the car, Pop," said Eddie, handing over the keys.

"Oh, thanks, Eddie," said his father. They all climbed into the car. Eddie sat between his father and mother.

For some time they drove in silence. Then Eddie said, "Well, I had a very enjoyable time."

Mr. and Mrs. Wilson immediately looked down at Eddie. He looked up at them with a sweet smile.

Mr. Wilson put on the brakes and stopped the car. He looked around on the back seat of the car and on the floor. There was nothing there.

"What did you say, Eddie?" his father asked.

Eddie looked up. "I just said I've had a very enjoyable time."

Mr. Wilson took the keys from the car. He walked around and opened the trunk. There was Eddie's package.

Eddie said, "Please, Pop, it isn't junk. It's swell stuff."

"Eddie, when I said, 'No more junk,' I meant it." To Eddie's amazement, his father placed the package in a ditch beside the road.

As Mr. Wilson leaned over, he saw the end of the lamp sticking out of the top of the box. He pulled off the cord and lifted out the lamp.

"Say!" he cried. "Why, this is a carriage lamp.

I have been wanting one of these for a long time. I want it to go on the post at the front gate. Why, this is a beautiful carriage lamp. It just needs to be refinished. Well, now!"

"But I bought it, Pop," said Eddie. "I paid for it."

"Well, I'll give you a dollar for it, Eddie," said his father. "How is that?"

"Okay!" said Eddie.

Mrs. Wilson joined Eddie and his father.

"Look, Mother!" Mr. Wilson cried. "Look at this fine carriage lamp. This is mine."

Mrs. Wilson was busy looking into the box. "Why, look at this old coffee grinder!" she cried. "Oh this is mine! These old coffee grinders make the most beautiful lamps you ever saw! With a coat of red paint, this will be perfect."

"But I bought it, Mamma," said Eddie. "I paid for it."

"Oh, well. I'll give you a dollar for it," said his mother. "Is a dollar all right?"

"Ah, Mamma!" said Eddie. "I like that coffee grinder. I like it a lot."

"Well, I'll give you two dollars for it," said his mother. "That's a lot of money, Eddie."

"Okay!" said Eddie.

The three went back to the car. Mr. Wilson went first, carrying his carriage lamp. Then Mrs. Wilson, carrying her coffee grinder. Little Eddie brought up the rear, with three dollars in his small fist.

"By the way, Eddie," Mr. Wilson said, "How much did you pay for that lamp?"

"A quarter," said Eddie.

"And how much did you pay for the coffee grinder?" asked his father.

"Fifty cents," Eddie replied.

"Not bad!" said his father, looking at his mother.

"You know, Pop!" said Eddie. "I've been thinking. Do you know what I'm going to be when I grow up?"

"No," replied Mr. Wilson. "What are you going to be?"

"I'm going to be a junk man," said Eddie. "That's a good way to get rich."

Stop and Think

1. What did Eddie call all the things he collected? What did his father call them?

2. What did Eddie buy at the antique shop?

3. Where did Eddie hide the things he had bought?

4. How much profit did Eddie make on the carriage lamp and coffee grinder?

HOLDING HANDS

Elephants walking
Along the trails

Are holding hands
By holding tails.

Trunks and tails
Are handy things

When elephants walk
In Circus rings.

Elephants work
And elephants play

And elephants bathe
And swim all day.

And when they walk—
It never fails

They're holding
hands
By holding tails.

—*Lenore M. Link*

THE HAIRY DOG

My dog's so furry I've not seen
His face for years and years:
His eyes are buried out of sight,
I only guess his ears.

When people ask me for his breed,
I do not know or care:
He has the beauty of them all
Hidden beneath his hair.

—*Herbert Asquith*

Word Watch   archbishop

Jonathan Bing

Poor old Jonathan Bing
Went out in his carriage
   to visit the King,
But everyone pointed and said,
   "Look at that!
Jonathan Bing has forgotten his
    hat!"
(He'd forgotten his hat!)

Poor old Jonathan Bing
Went home and put on a new hat
   for the King.
But up by the palace
   a soldier said, "Hi!
You can't see the King;
   you've forgotten your tie!"
(He'd forgotten his tie!)

Poor old Jonathan Bing
He put on a *beautiful* tie
   for the King,
But when he arrived,
   an Archbishop said, "Ho!
You can't come to court
   in pajamas, you know!"

Poor old Jonathan Bing
Went home and addressed
   a short note to the King:
   "If you please will excuse me
I won't come to tea;
   For home's the best place for
All people like me!"

—*B. Curtis Brown*

For the King

One stormy night many years ago, an old woman and her two sons sat in their little cottage in Scotland. The room was small and the furniture poor, but a bright fire burned on the hearth, and the little home looked neat and cozy.

The mother sat at her spinning wheel, but anyone watching her closely could see that her mind was not on her work. Every now and again she glanced at her two sons who were preparing their bows and arrows for a hunt the next day, so they had said, and were whispering together.

At last the mother stopped her work and asked, "What is the matter, my sons? Why do you whisper together and look so grave?"

"Matter enough, mother," answered Malcolm, the elder son. "The English army is encamped but two miles from our village."

"Aye," continued Donald, "and if they come this way, tomorrow may see us driven out into the heath."

"And what if we should be driven from our home!" cried the mother. "Are we any better than our good king? Even tonight he wanders through this raging storm with no place to lay his head."

A loud knock followed immediately on her words. She hastened to open the door. A man closely muffled in a cloak stood without.

"My good woman," he said, "may I come in from the storm?"

"Come in. You are right welcome," she said. "For the sake of one who wanders abroad this wild night, I gladly receive you."

The stranger entered and stood before the fire, his face still covered by a fold of his long cloak.

"For whose sake am I welcome?" he asked.

"For the sake of our good king, Robert the Bruce, who is hunted like a wild beast by the English," cried the old woman. "How glad would my heart be to know that he has found shelter this stormy night."

"Then, Dame, be of good cheer. Robert Bruce is sheltered and is even now within your own home. I am Robert Bruce." As he spoke, the king dropped his cloak to the ground and stood smiling at the old woman.

"You! You, our king!" she cried. "Where are your followers? Why are you alone?"

"Alas! I have no followers now. All have been driven away. I travel alone," answered the king.

"Nay, my king, that you shall no longer do!" exclaimed the good woman. "Here are my two sons!

"Malcolm, Donald, behold your king. When he leaves, go with him; serve him; follow him to the death, if need be!"

The two young men stepped forward and

knelt before the king, who placed a hand on each head as a sign that he accepted them as loyal followers.

As they rose to their feet, they were startled by hearing loud voices outside the door.

"It is the English!" whispered the mother, throwing her full weight against the door. "Defend your king, my sons! Fight for him! Protect him to the last!"

Quickly the young men caught up heavy clubs and placed themselves before the king.

"Open! open!" cried a voice from without, and a heavy hand struck the door.

"Open, open, my good woman," repeated the king. "That is no English voice, but the voice of my brother, Edward Bruce."

The door was opened at once and the king's brother and his friend, the Earl of Douglas, entered the room.

They were overjoyed to find the king, whom they had been seeking. After greeting him, they cried: "Hasten, my lord; we have with us one hundred fifty men—enough to give the English an unpleasant surprise this night. We need only you to be our leader."

"One hundred fifty-two men," answered the king, pointing to the two Scottish youths. "These new friends of mine are brave and faithful. They will go with us."

"Aye, go, my sons," said the old woman, "and remember that your mother has sent you out to fight and, if need be, to die for the king!"

"For the king!" repeated the young men, following Robert the Bruce from the room.

The two young Scots rose rapidly to fame and served the king until every English soldier was driven from the land and Robert Bruce reigned once more the king of Scotland.

Stop and Think

1. For whose sake did the Scottish woman welcome the stranger into her home?

2. Who did the woman say would go with the king and defend him when he left?

3. What good news did the king's brother, Edward Bruce, bring?

Breakfast with Buffalo Bill

Bill Cody was a daredevil rider, one of the youngest of the boys who rode for the Pony Express. He was also a crack shot. He earned his nickname, Buffalo Bill, by killing thousands of buffaloes to provide meat for railway workers. Later, he became famous all over the United States and Europe as manager of the "Wild West Show." In this show, cowboys, Indians, and western ponies acted out the dangerous life of the pioneer on the Great Plains.

About ten minutes to four, in that darkest time before the dawn, the first whistle of the *Wild West* train sounded down the valley.

Ardeth stirred in her bed. Then a shower of pebbles struck her window and brought her wide awake.

"Hey, there!" a voice called from below.

Ardeth ran to the window. Below on the lawn were the shadowy forms of Martin and Henry Dawlish.

"Hurry up!" hissed Martin. "It's nearly in. We'll miss the fun."

Ardeth flung on her clothes, shivering with excitement. In a moment she was hurrying down the dark street between Martin and Henry. The whistle of the *Wild West* train shrieked twice from the other side of town.

"We shook hands with Buffalo Bill last year in Montana," said Henry.

Ardeth had heard this several times before, but it always thrilled her. "Do you think he'll remember you?" she asked.

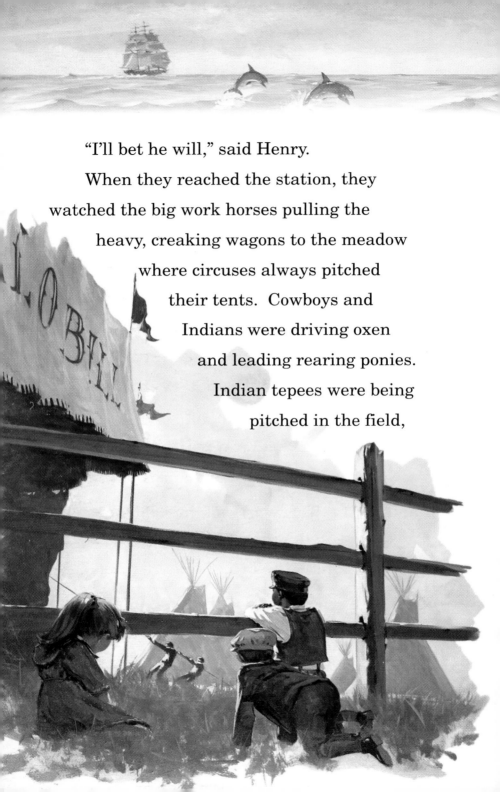

"I'll bet he will," said Henry.

When they reached the station, they
watched the big work horses pulling the
heavy, creaking wagons to the meadow
where circuses always pitched
their tents. Cowboys and
Indians were driving oxen
and leading rearing ponies.
Indian tepees were being
pitched in the field,

and the enormous show tent was going up to the sound of shouts and grunts.

"Let's go and watch the cowboys have their breakfast," said Martin.

"Breakfast?" asked Ardeth. "Do they eat?"

"Sure. You can't move shows and do trick riding, and shooting, and bronco-busting without food, you know," said Martin.

The first tent to be completely set up was the dining tent. In a few moments the three stood by the open flap of the tent watching the cooks in their greasy white caps and aprons making breakfast. To her delight, Ardeth saw that they fried their ham and flipped their pancakes right on the tops of the stoves.

The *Wild West* people came in as they found time and sat down at bare wooden tables. It was like a picnic every day. There was a girl there in divided skirt and cowboy hat who might have been Annie Oakley, the sure-fire shot, herself. There were Indians, too, eating ham and eggs as peacefully as the cowboys. Just opposite the children sat a cowboy with a purple shirt and a ten-gallon hat. He was reading a paper-covered book called *The Life and Death of Jesse James, the Outlaw.*

Martin sniffed the good smell of frying ham and bacon. "I sure would like some breakfast," he said, "but I can't spare the time to go home."

"Oh, no," said Ardeth. "Let's not go home!"

Hard-Headed Henry

Just then Henry let out a whoop of delight and began to run.

"Buffalo Bill!" he yelled.

Across the meadow from the main tent cantered a white horse carrying a very erect rider with long white hair beneath his wide-brimmed hat. Colonel William Cody, the buffalo hunter, the scout who had fought off Indian attacks, was riding in to get his breakfast.

"It's Buffalo Bill!" said Martin. "It sure is!"

Henry ran on, his arms spread wide, shouting: "Buffalo Bill, you 'member me? I shook hands with you last year in Mon—"

The horse was coming faster than Henry had realized. Frightened by a blowing paper, it swerved suddenly and knocked him down. He rolled over and over on the dusty grass, and lay still.

Ardeth screamed, and Martin began to run. The old scout reined in his horse and cantered back. A little crowd gathered.

For a moment Henry lay quiet, his face white.

"Henry!" called Martin. "Henry! Henry!"

Then Henry sat up, shaking his head,
"—last year in Montana," he finished.

Buffalo Bill sprang off his horse and bent
over him. "Well, now, young feller, you kind
of ran amuck, didn't you?" he said.

"He was so glad to see you," explained
Martin to Buffalo Bill. "Once he got his head

caught in a cider press, but it didn't hurt him. Mama says he's got the Dawlish skull—you can't crack it."

"Can you stand up?" asked the Colonel. "No bones broken?"

Henry stood up and dusted himself off. "I reckon I'm all here," he said.

"What's all this about Montana?"

"Martin and I shook your hand then. Don't you remember?"

"Well, I'm an old man, now, Bud. My memory's not what it used to be."

"I told you he wouldn't remember," said Martin.

"Oh," said Henry. "I had on my new straw hat, too."

"Well, no wonder!" said the Colonel. "How was I to know you without your hat? I've shook thousands of boys' hands since last summer. Had your breakfast?"

"No, sir, and we've been up since four."

"Come along, then. We'll see what we can do."

Ham and Eggs for Four!

Ardeth had an awful pang of fear. They were going off without her! She gave a little gasp, and Martin turned around and remembered her.

"This is Ardeth," he said politely. "She's never had the pleasure of shaking your hand."

"Petticoats, eh?" said the Colonel.

"She's all right," said Henry loyally. "She has a pony, and she knows how to ride it."

"That's different then. Shake hands, my girl."

Ardeth felt her hand being gripped hard by the very hand which had hunted so many buffaloes. In a daze of delight, she followed along to the dining tent.

As for the food, ham and eggs and

buckwheat cakes had never tasted better.
This was the meal of a lifetime!

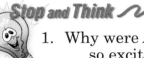

Stop and Think

1. Why were Ardeth, Martin, and Henry so excited?

2. Why did Henry think Buffalo Bill would know him?

3. What happened when Henry ran to meet Buffalo Bill?

4. What did Buffalo Bill mean when he said, "Petticoats, eh?"

Word Watch

Nareela (nə·rē′lə)

	heathen	parades
	rickety	vigorously
beckoned	practically	terrified
immediately	fervently	amuse

pelt: to throw

The Missionary with the Orange Hair

A Story of India

Nareela lives in India where it is warm and rainy all year 'round. Nareela wears a simple blue cotton frock with a long scarf which covers her head and drapes across both shoulders. Nareela's house has a grass roof and the pigs and chickens walk in and out as they please. Sometimes even the thin brown cow comes in to visit, and no one dares shoo her out, for they believe a cow is holy!

Nareela is smiling today, but it is not very often that she can smile. Nareela's mother has decided to sell her to the heathen temple to be a servant of the gods.

"You will have pretty clothes to wear," her mother coaxed, "and you will ride in the big parades, perhaps on top of an elephant."

"That may be true," Nareela thought, "but what a terrible life it will be; living in the dark, dirty temple, taking care of the ugly stone idols. And they don't have parades every day, either."

But Nareela did not dare say anything aloud. Today, she was especially happy. She had a holiday from work—nothing to do but play. She had a few pennies of her own and started off for the market place.

What is this? An old man sitting in the road making pottery—all kinds and shapes of jugs and bowls. The old man had a red turban

wrapped around his head and down to his
eyebrows to keep his head from the hot sun.
'Round and 'round spun the
potter's wheel and soon
there was a smooth jar.
The potter set the
jar to bake
in the fire
and then painted
it a bright
orange. "It
would be so pretty to carry water in," said
Nareela to herself. "But it costs so much. I
don't even have enough money to buy a small
dish."

The old man offered her the pretty
orange jar and pointed to Nareela's bracelets,
but Nareela did not take them off, even at
night. She thought they would protect her
from the anger of the evil spirits and from

having any accident. Nareela shook her head fearfully and turned her back on the orange jar. Better to never have a pretty water jar than to take off her metal and glass bracelets.

An ox cart came slowly into sight and Nareela begged a ride. The man was kind and let Nareela hop into the wooden cart with the big thick wheels. The rickety old cart bumped and nearly shook Nareela to pieces, but she thought it was the most fun she ever had. She just wished the clumsy old oxen would walk faster.

Ummm, Yummm, all children like penny candy and Nareela was no different from you boys and girls. In the marketplace sat a candy seller in one corner, sheltered from the glaring sun, and Nareela jumped down from the ox cart and hurried toward him.

Here were little sweet cakes, cookies, and buns. They were sticky globs of taffy and

little hard balls. Nareela stopped by the counter and tried to pick out her favorite kind but it was so hard to decide. Everything looked so good. The man looked angry and shook his head vigorously when Nareela touched the candies. He weighed the candy on his old-fashioned scales to make sure he wasn't giving Nareela too many!

Nareela sucked the sweets and walked slowly through the marketplace. A crowd was gathering around a white man with a book and Nareela ran over to see what was happening. She had seen the missionary before and noticed that he always carried a big black book.

"That's his book of magic," someone in the crowd whispered. "The man couldn't work magic without his black book."

Nareela stared at the missionary. She

wished he would work magic now. She wondered if she would be afraid and run, if he did. The missionary wore brown shorts and high brown socks. He had a bright green shirt and a funny flat hat, like a plate on his head. He wore no turban, and Nareela wondered how he kept his head cool. His arms were bare and so pale. Perhaps he had scrubbed all the color off.

The missionary didn't say anything or open his book this time. Instead, he beckoned with his finger to someone back of him. A smaller figure in a short dress came forward, and—why, what in the world!—it was a lady missionary, the first the people had ever seen. She must belong to the missionary man. And of all things—the crowd chattered and pointed and nudged each other in awe! Nareela stretched her neck to see. All of a

sudden she felt such a shock of surprise that
she almost lost her balance and tumbled over
on her nose. The lady
missionary had orange
hair! Orange!
Bright orange,
just like the
pretty jar the potter
had for sale.

The crowd became
louder and some began to
jeer at the missionary.
"Orange-head," they
sneered, pointing long
brown fingers of scorn at the missionary lady,
who merely smiled at them.

"Magic!" shrilled an old Indian woman,
turning to run, but the crowd was so thick
that she could scarcely move.

"Devils!" shrieked another, and a few bent to pick up stones and clods of mud.

Nareela didn't know what to do. The man had put his arm around the lady missionary and had stepped in front of her. The missionary lady closed her eyes and put her hands in front of her face. The magic is about to begin, thought Nareela excitedly. She forgot to be afraid.

Someone in the crowd said, "I saw them hang up a white sheet one night and make shadows dance and talk on it. They can put every kind of noise into a box."

"Stone them!" called another. "Stone them out of town!"

The people had begun to pelt them with stones. Nareela became more and more excited as she listened to the screaming and cries of the men and women. The lady with

the orange hair must be an evil spirit. If they
didn't kill her, she might put a curse on the
village, or cause the crops to fail, or kill the pigs
and chickens. Nareela found an opening in the
crowd, fighting her way through. When she
was practically next to the lady missionary, she
hurled a stone, striking her on the side of the
face. The missionary gave a little cry and held
a small piece of white cloth to her face.

Nareela turned to dart away, but the
missionary with the orange hair seized her
with both arms and would not let her go.

Nareela fought to free herself. What
would the missionary do to her? She might
even kill Nareela because she had thrown the
stone. She struggled and kicked and even
tried biting, but the missionary lady held her
fast and at last Nareela was forced to pause
for breath. She was terrified.

The lady missionary leaned down to look into Nareela's face. "Well, little one," she said gently, "aren't you tired yet?"

Nareela couldn't answer. She hid her face from the missionary and began to cry. Why wasn't the missionary angry? Why didn't she beat her? Was she going to work magic and turn her into a tree?

"Come, little fighting rooster," said the missionary as she smiled. The crowd had lost courage and drifted away. The missionary with the orange hair still held tightly to Nareela's arm. "Come over to my house, it isn't far," she urged. "I will give you a pretty picture."

Nareela looked fearfully at the missionary's face, but the cut had stopped bleeding and didn't look serious at all. "Come," the missionary said again. "I won't hurt you. I love you."

When they reached the house, the missionary brought out beautifully colored pictures of a man holding out his arms to the little children.

"This is Jesus, God's Son," explained the lady. "He loves you. He died for you."

"Loves me?" Nareela repeated. "Does He like me?"

"Jesus **loves** you," corrected the missionary.

Then, seeing that Nareela did not understand, she said: "When you threw the stone at me, and struck me in the face, what did I do?"

Nareela felt a flush of shame come to her cheek. "You took me in your arms and held me tight and wouldn't let me go," she whispered.

"That is love," said the missionary softly. "And Jesus loves you more than I do!"

"More?"

"Yes, Jesus died for your sin, your badness. Then He came back to life and is watching you, even now."

Nareela never knew before that anyone loved her. Now two people loved her; the missionary and Jesus. And Jesus loved her most. It was really a wonderful feeling, to be so happy.

"You can talk to Jesus," the missionary

lady went on. "Tell Him that you believe in Him, and thank Him for dying for you."

"Where is He?" asked Nareela, looking around.

"He can't be seen," was the missionary's answer. "But if you trust in Him, He will save you from your sin, and come to live in your heart."

Nareela thought she would like that. She didn't understand all of it, but if this Jesus loved her, then she would trust Him. So she shut her eyes tight and prayed.

As she lifted her head, she thought immediately of her parents. "Let's tell them," she begged the missionary. "Does Jesus love them?"

"Yes," replied the missionary. "He loves the whole world."

Soon the missionary was at Nareela's

house. Only her mother was home, getting supper ready for the men. She spread a straw mat in the middle of the floor, placed a deep bowl as large as a dishpan in the center, and poured all the food into it.

The men always ate first, Nareela and her mother eating what happened to be left.

Nareela's mother looked up in surprise as Nareela took the missionary by the hand and led her through the low doorway, into the humble, one-room house.

"Tell her," Nareela commanded the missionary eagerly. "Tell her who loves her."

Nareela's mother stared in surprise at the missionary's orange hair. She couldn't take her eyes from the strange sight. Like Nareela, she too, was a little afraid, but the kind words of the missionary lady made her feel at ease. As the missionary told the wonderful story of Jesus' love for her, Nareela's mother drank in every word. It wasn't long before she, too, knelt on the mud floor and gave her heart to Jesus.

"Now you won't sell me to the temple, will you?" was the first thing Nareela asked, as they arose from their knees. "You won't send me away from home, will you?"

"Oh no," her mother replied fervently. "That was before I knew of Jesus. Now I know the temple is an evil place. The people there do not know of Jesus' love. They would be very cruel to you. No, no, I could not think of selling you to the temple, now."

Both Nareela and the missionary were very glad. "Here," said Nareela, pulling off her metal and glass bracelets. "I want to give these to Jesus. I don't want them any more. They cannot protect me from evil spirits. I am not afraid to take them off."

She pulled them off her arm and dropped them into the missionary's hand. "If you cannot use them for something good, then throw them away," she said bravely. "I cannot wear them anymore, since I know Jesus."

Nareela's mother was still studying the missionary's orange hair. "Is it real?" she finally asked.

The missionary lady laughed and tugged with both hands at her bright hair. "It's real, as God made it," she assured her.

"Why, I never would have met you, or heard of Jesus, if I hadn't noticed your orange hair, and stopped to look," said Nareela.

This seemed to amuse the missionary.
"Then it's good for something," she said, with
a pleased look.

Stop and Think

1. What country does Nareela live in?

2. What had Nareela's mother decided to
    do that had made Nareela very un-
    happy?

3. Why did the crowd point and laugh at the
    missionary lady?

4. After Nareela threw the stone that
    struck the missionary lady in the
    face, what did the missionary lady do?

5. How did Nareela's mother show that
    Jesus had changed her heart?

One Gentle Word

One gentle word that we may speak,
   Or one kind, loving deed,
May, though a trifle, poor and weak,
   Prove like a tiny seed;
And who can tell what good may spring
From such a very little thing?

BEDTIME

Do you know how many children
   Go to little beds at night,
And, without a care or trouble,
   Wake up with the morning bright?
God in heaven each name can tell;
   Knows you, too, and loves you well.

Credits

"America, Our Country" by Dorothy Hall in *Magic Carpet,*
copyright 1966 by Charles E. Merrill Co., reprinted by permission of The McGraw-Hill Companies, Inc. "Any Old Junk
Today?" from *Little Eddie* by Carolyn Haywood, copyright ©1947
by Carolyn Haywood, by permission of Morrow Junior Books, a
division of William Morrow & Company, Inc. "Books" reprinted
by permission of Harold Ober Associates Incorporated, copyright
1938 by Eleanor Farjeon, copyright renewed 1966 by Gervase
Farjeon. "Breakfast with Buffalo Bill" reprinted with the
permission of Simon & Schuster Books for Young Readers, an
imprint of Simon & Schuster Children's Publishing Division
from *All Over Town* by Carol Ryrie Brink; copyright 1939
Macmillan Publishing Company; copyright renewed ©1967
Carol Ryrie Brink. "Christmas with the Angels" taken from
Treasures of the Snow by Patricia St. John, Moody Bible
Institute of Chicago; Moody Press; used by permission. "The
Cricket in Times Square" excerpted from *The Cricket in Times
Square* (approx. 1590 words from pages 22–32) by George Seldon
(Puffin, 1963). Copyright © 1960 by George Seldon Thompson
and Garth Williams, copyright renewed © 1988 by George
Seldon Thompson, reprinted by permission of Farrar, Straus &
Giroux, Inc., and Penguin Books Ltd. "A Good Traveller"
reprinted by permission of Cynthia Nadelman for the estate of
Frances Cavanaugh. "Hector and His Conscience" reprinted by
permission of Bible Club Movement, Inc. from *Reporter,* April
1969. "Jonathan Bing" copyright 1936 by Oxford University
Press, renewed ©1964 by Beatrice Curtis Brown, reproduced by
permission of Curtis Brown, London. "Kitten-in-a-Basket" by
Elizabeth Coatsworth from *The Giant Golden Book of Cat
Stories,* © 1953 Golden Books Publishing Company, Inc., used by
permission. "Lost in the Apple Cave" from *Children of the
Handicrafts* by Carolyn Sherwin Bailey, lithographs by Grace
Paull; copyright 1935 by Carolyn Sherwin Bailey, renewed 1962
by Rebecca Davies Ryan; used by permission of Viking Penguin,
a division of Penguin Books USA Inc. "The Missionary with the
Orange Hair" reprinted by permission of Dr. Paul Wharton,
published by Higley Publishing Company. "Only the Stars and
the Sea Gulls" which originally appeared in *Pulpit Digest,*
reprinted by permission of Logos Productions Inc. "The Pasture"
by Robert Frost from *The Poetry of Robert Frost,* edited by
Edward Connery Lathem; copyright 1939, ©1967, 1969 by
Henry Holt & Co., Inc.; reprinted by permission of Henry Holt &
Co., Inc., the Estate of the Author and Jonathan Cape, publisher.
"Some One" by Walter de la Mare reprinted by permission of The
Literary Trustees of Walter de la Mare, and The Society of
Authors as their representative. "The Town Crier and the
Tailor" from *The Elephant's Friend and Other Stories* from *The
Children's Bookshelf,* compiled and edited by B. R. Buckingham,
copyright, 1934, by Ginn and Company; used by permission of
Silver Burdett Ginn Inc.